H. Marten
D1458280

Ca

Fourth Book of Children's Poetry

Beaver Books

A Beaver Book
Published by Arrow Books Limited
62-5 Chandos Place, London WC2N 4NW
An imprint of Century Hutchinson Ltd

London Melbourne Sydney Auckland
Johannesburg and agencies throughout the world

First published 1986
© Cadbury Ltd 1986

This book is sold subject to the condition that it shall not, by way of trade or otherwise, be lent resold, hired out, or otherwise circulated without the publisher's prior consent in any form of binding or cover other than that in which it is published and without a similar condition including this condition being imposed on the subsequent purchaser.

Set in Souvenir Light by
JH Graphics Limited, Reading

Made and printed in Great Britain
by Cox & Wyman Limited, Reading

ISBN 0 09 947750 5

which give the reader the opportunity to compare the ideas of children from as young as five to mature seventeen year olds. All the illustrations are taken from entries to the Art and Craft section of this year's Exhibition, and they complement the poems in an unusual and satisfying way.

We are very pleased to be publishing such an interesting and original book and would like to thank all the writers and artists for their superb efforts. Don't forget, there's another chance to see your poem in print in the fifth *Cadbury's Book of Poetry* to be published in 1987. For details on how to enter next year's competition please turn to page 221.

Cadbury Limited and the Publishers have taken every possible precaution to ensure that the material in this book is the original work of the named writers and does not infringe the copyright of any person or body. Each poem has been authenticated by a responsible adult and the work has been carefully checked by independent experts for plagiarism. If, despite this, we have inadvertently failed to identify any borrowed poem we would be grateful if this could be brought to our attention for correction at the first opportunity.

Foreword

The National Exhibition of Children's Art, now in its fortieth year, was built upon the principle that 'child art' should be recognized and viewed as 'art' in its own right.

Four years ago, we at Cadbury recognized that we could extend this principle to the written word. We expanded our sponsorship to include a poetry section in the hope that this would help broaden the adult's view and understanding of young, talented artists.

The Fourth Book of Children's Poetry is evidence of the talent and interest which abounds. Both committees of judges had an enjoyable but difficult task in choosing the final selection. We thank them for their work. We also thank the teachers and parents who encourage and nurture young talent to the high standards we see today.

Most importantly, we would like to thank all the young poets who have submitted their work for consideration.

Royalties from the publication of *Cadbury's Fourth Book of Children's Poetry* will be donated to the Save the Children Fund.

Adrian Cadbury

Cadbury's Fourth Book of Children's Poetry

AWARD WINNERS – Poetry Section

39th National Exhibition of Children's Art 1986/87

1986 ITALIAN TOUR AWARD

Catherine Skinner (16)
Hitchin, Herts

Adam Stanley (15)
Minehead, Somerset

SCHOOL POETRY AWARD

The King's School Canterbury, Kent

HIGHLY COMMENDED

7 and under

James Casswell (7) Browns School, Sleaford, Lincs
Helen M. Shires (7) Bedgrove County First School, Aylesbury, Bucks

8-11

Nicholas Perks (11) Dalkeith, Lothian

12-14

Andrew Holgate Darley (13) The King's School, Canterbury, Kent
Johnathan F. Ibbott (14) The King's School, Canterbury, Kent

15-17

Arnold Hunt (16) Hendon, London
Christopher Jones (16) Quorn, Leicestershire
Adam Moon (16) Pilsley, Nr Chesterfield, Derbyshire

Me

Kate

My surname is Todd,
My Christian name is Kate,
I live at 'Little Acre',
I am eight.
We live in the country
With pretty lanes and passes;
And by the way
I have glasses.

Kate Todd (8)
Herne C.P.E. School,
Herne, Kent

Birthdays

At nine months
My life was confused,
Amid screams and blood
I was born.

Although with little understanding,
I enjoyed my birthday
At three.
On piles of card and paper
I slept smiling.

When I was seven
My party was a thrill
Of oranges and sherbet,
Musical statues and
A cake full of candles.

By ten, birthdays had become serious.
Ordered swimming trips replaced
Riotous, unregulated tumbles.
My own satisfaction lost through
Concern for others' pleasure.

And now that day passes
Quietly, semi-forgotten.
At fifteen I plough through homework
Deserted by my party friends
And the candles
Too numerous
Are extinguished.

Adam Stanley (15)
The West Somerset School, Minehead, Somerset
(Award Winner)

'Self Portrait', Gaynor Francis (16)

The Blanket

Thirteen years ago, my grandmother knitted a blanket:
Old balls of wool materialized from her sewing box,
Which smelt of mothballs and cobwebs.
She gave it to me for my birthday:
Some patches were striped and
My mother said it looked like Joseph's coat,
And my father joked that he wanted it for his car.
I took it to bed with me,
And every night my mother played counting and colour games.
When she asked what colour, I would reply correctly,
But when it was red, I would always answer:
'Best red'
And in the end I called it that,
And took it wherever I went.
When I had been naughty, and sent to my room,
I talked to it, but it never answered.
I brought it when we visited people.
My brother was sick over it in the car,
And my mother wanted to throw it out of the window,
But I refused,
And our hostess washed it for me.

That night, when I didn't have it,
I kept on crying;
My mother said it was due to being in a strange house,
But I knew it was due to Best Red's absence.
One day, my mother said I was too old for it,
And gave it to my brother,
(After he'd gone crying to her, saying I'd hit him).
For a week, I suffered, and then a rabbit took its place.

Many years later, I had forgotten about Best Red;
My brother had quickly grown tired of it,
And I thought my treacherous mother had given it
To a jumble sale,
Or thrown it in the dustbin to rot.
But searching through a chest of drawers,
I found it full of mothballs,
Which showed my mother had really cared . . .

Julien Foster (14)
The King's School,
Canterbury, Kent

Reflections

I've often sat and wondered,
When I'm walking near a lake,
Who is that reflection,
It doesn't look awake.

It just slides there, glides there,
And when I move it hides there,
I suppose there's no connection,
Between me and my reflection.

Donna Hill (12)
Canon Maggs C. E. Middle School
Bedworth, Warwicks

My Mirror

Anonymous I came to you;
You clothed me with humanity.
Others labelled me, condemned me,
But you are the all-perceiving.
You probed my outer skin, revealed
To me my personality,
So that I can stand tall and say,
'Look! This is me; I live; I breathe;
No longer an automaton.'
Your knowledge has bestowed on me
That precious gift – identity.

Clare Connors (14)
Debenham High School,
Stowmarket, Suffolk

The Reef

When waters are troubled
I prefer to be beneath –
Rather than building bridges
I feel that I'm a reef;
Spread below the tempest
I miss exhilarating shows,
But polyp by slow polyp
The hiddden power grows.
I've sunk beneath their notice
To them I'm less than zero
In a bank account; who cares,
I don't need to be a hero.
And they sail on – driven
By their wind of ambition,
Throw waves on to the shore
And demand attention.
I'm just biding my time
All my energy in growing,
Warped, perhaps, and sharp;
But they've no way of knowing
Still water runs not deep,
At least not here, where I,
Though hidden and forgotten,
Can steal them from the sky
And bring them to these depths.
For one day they must slip –
One day I'll achieve something
And wreck their bloody ship.

Sophie Kyle (17)
Slough, Bucks

Secrets

In the priestholes of my mind
  I hide
    my secrets,
Dark threads of subjects no one knows,
My private thoughts.
Nobody knows of my den in the tree,
How I dream of the clouds in the sky,
How I wish – not for the wings of a
    dove – but an albatross
    swooping on high.
Oh what would it be like to go to the moon?
How I wish there were aliens in space.
In the safes of my mind
I hide the ingots of my secrets.

Felicity Hines (14)
Convent of Our Lady of Providence,
Alton, Hants

My Resentment

My resentment is like a bubble that cannot burst,
Floating around with nowhere to roam,
Building up pressure inside all the time,
Feeling the agitating blankness of not knowing what to
do,
The stress of being incapable of bursting,
But it goes as the bubble slowly lands on a thistle.

Rachael Brown (13)
Chantry High School,
Ipswich, Suffolk

'Swimming', Nicola Frost (5)

Don't Want To!

'Richard!
Do this.
Richard!
Do that.'
'Don't want to!'
'Don't answer me back!'

I don't want to
Come to school,
Wash my face,
Make my bed,
Tie up my lace.

But it's –
'Richard!
Do this.
Richard!
Do that.'
'Don't want to!'
'Don't answer me back!'

Richard Evans (11)
Grenoside Junior School,
Sheffield, Yorks.

When I Am Angry

When I get angry I start
    screaming
and screeching
    raging
and hating
    smashing
and biting
    crying
and punching
    leaving
and breaking
    throwing
and destroying
    steamed up
and blowing up
    slam doors
and stamping
    exploding
and strangling
    cuddling
and kissing
    sorrys
and quiet again.

Ian White (8)
Buxlow Prep School,
Wembley, Middx

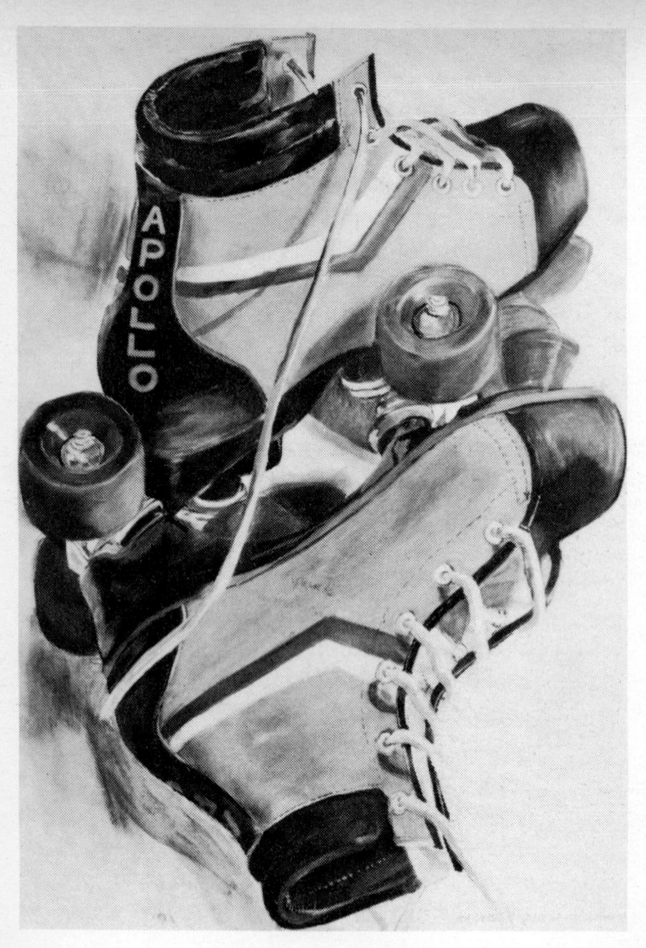

'Roller Boots', *Elizabeth Greenwood (16)*

When I Blow My Own Trumpet

When I blow my own trumpet,
the doorbell rings and the telephone rings,
everyone tries to pick up the phone and open
the door.

When I blow my own trumpet,
in the street everyone disappears into a shop,
all the windows shut and start chattering as
if they were laughing, and my dog howls.

When I blow my own trumpet,
my mum pulls her hat over her ears, my
brother skis down the lane, my dog sinks
down under the table, and my cat races up
a tree.

When I blow my own trumpet,
the clock spins madly, my brother jumps
out of the window, the book falls off the
shelf and a tree falls down as if it
has fainted.

When I blow my own trumpet,
my whole family rush for the china and
run out of the room and John Wayne falls off
his horse.

Claire Bayntun (9)
Freda Gardham C.P. School,
Rye, Sussex

Failure

The queue stretched on.
The boys shoved out their hands
For the master to inspect.
He tugged a shirt
Which was then hastily shoved in.
I knew he'd caught me
Out of the corner of his eye,
But he wouldn't give it away,
Not yet anyway.
One person nearer.
Now another . . .
Now another . . .
The smell of the greasy food
Combined with my fear
To constrict and torture my stomach,
As if by this very action
It could squeeze out
All nervousness
And the possibility of failure.
But then he might not know,
Although of course he must, I knew
By the way he was avoiding my eyes.
'I've got some news,
From your next school.
You see we've got inside information.'
He grinned at his own joke.
'I'm afraid it's not good.'
He knew he didn't have to say any more.
I understood it,
But could not contort my features
Into the dismay and hurt I felt,
Leaving them

In their innocent inquisitive pose.
'Perhaps it might be wrong, sir?'
The boy behind me's remark
Only crushed hope even more.
'I'm afraid not.'
The simple remark
Was the key
To release my muscles
From their self-imposed immobility.
I moved on,
Head slumped,
Shoulders pushed forward.
For some reason
The master felt guilty:
I could sense his worried glances
At my retreating figure.
I wanted to get away
On my own,
Just to think what it meant
But my friends at the table
Wouldn't leave me,
Not realizing that by their comforting
They did me harm.
It took a long time
To really accept it,
But now I realize
You have to fail . . .
Sometime.

Jonathan F. Ibbott (14)
The King's School,
Canterbury, Kent
(Highly commended)

The Literary Vandal

I am not the sort of youth
Who has to scrawl
His name
Upon every lavatory wall
He's ever been in.
Nor, indeed,
Do I feel the need
To be able
To enscribe 'Stephen 4 so-and-so'
On every available
Spot of table.
Who would wish to be
The desk-top poet,
When I have the power
To be the fully fledged
Vandal of literature?
And with every written word
I etch my mark upon society.
(True, 'tis only shallow,
But then, isn't society, these days?)
And on every page
I record 'I love Miss X!'
In innumerable different ways,
As either poetry, prose,
Or profundity.

My one eternal message,
Cast in black ink
On white cartridge paper;
Winner of the Nobel Prize
For the best example
Of literary graffiti.

Stephen Lee (16)
The Aelfgar School,
Rugeley, Staffs

Thumbs Down

A year ago I mislaid my thumbs,
You know the fingers that aren't.
I pulled my hand from beneath the bed
and found five and six had departed.
Those irresponsible digits had gone and
left me disabled.
Without them how could I hitch a lift
Or pick up a pencil to draw?
Thumbs down to them, I say.

Mark Bell (10)
St Wilfrid's School
Haywards Heath, Sussex

Lost and Found

One hot summer,
a long time ago,
I wrote a poem,
no one will know.

It was the kind of poem,
I cannot forget,
and that's a kind of poem,
I know you've never met yet.

I hid it in the garden,
under the soil,
I dug a hole and buried it,
It was wrapped in tin foil.

I put a cross to mark the spot,
But that was trampled down,
So I will write another poem,
I'll call it 'Lost and found'.

Rachael Brown (13)
Chantry High School,
Ipswich, Suffolk

Feelings, Sensations

A Yawn

Breathe in,
Deep.
Pull in the tongue,
Arched,
Pop, ears go.
Yawn and stretch,
Open wider.
I can't control my mouth.
Eyes water,
Like a glass cover.
Nose tingles.
Hand comes up,
Hiding it.
Tongue starts stretching out,
Mouth closes,
With a hurricane of air.

That's Better!

Ashley Worthington (11)
The Beacon School,
Amersham, Bucks

Red is . . .

Red is . . .
like blood oozing from a man.
The Grenadier Guards saluting grandly.
Anger burning in my mind,
as I cry alone by myself . . .

Richard Pace (8)
St Stephen's School,
South Godstone, Surrey

Grey

The colour of a wet day
Of a distant peak
The colour of hardness
And of irrepressible hopelessness.

Nicholas Perks (11)
Dalkeith, Scotland
(Highly Commended)

Marble

If I fell into my marble
It would be like being in a maze
with over
                a thousand ways to go.
It would be like a mouse lost in a jungle.
It would be
                like swimming
In a world
                full of moons.

Kevin J. Mallen (9)
Freda Gardham C.P. School,
Rye, Sussex

My Imagination

My imagination is like a rocket
Zooming into space
Into a black hole
At the speed of light
Being zapped out of the air
And crashing into the planet of words
Creating new words or rockets
To get away.

Warren Tucker (9)
South Green Junior School,
Billericay, Essex

Trampoline

Travelling through the air
Rising quickly into the sky
Air rushing up and down against my cheek
Magnificently landing
Pleasant feeling
Overwhelmed
Lunging up
Imposing upon the birds
Nimbly letting my body fall
Excited and exhausted I step down.

Nicole Mathon (10)
Eleanor Palmer School
Kentish Town, London

'Fire Goddess', Vimmi Gupta (15)

Travel

I rode the waves,
on a surf-board of silence.

I flew round the world,
in a leopard moth of lies.

I skied down the mountain,
on skis of slowness.

I soared the sky,
on a hang-glider of height.

I sailed the sea,
in a boat of barnacles.

Nicholas Robus (10)
Freda Gardham C.P. School,
Rye, Sussex

The Tree Climb

The sun shining in my eyes,
I scrabble around the tree,
Looking for a branch stump.
I look up and see a branch,
Just out of reach.
I jump up and grab it.
It is wet and slimy.
My hands slip!
Wildly I grab,
But fall,
To land on my feet.
I look at my hands;
They are wet and slightly grazed.
The smell of wet bark and moss.
Again I try:
This time I get more grip.
I dangle like a helpless spider,
My feet walking up the tree until
They reach the branch.
I sit there for a while
And smell
The wet bark,
And hear
The leaves rustling like milk bottle tops.

And the sun is shining in my eyes.

Peter Watts (11)
Halesworth Middle School,
Halesworth, Suffolk

Candles

The candles flickering
And the candles
Reflect in your eyes.
The light of the candle
Makes me feel
I am in a holy place like a church.
It is very hot.
A candle smoulders,
Bright and hot.
The candle flickers,
In the halo.
The smoke drifts,
Up and up,
Turning and twirling around.

Peter Dummett (7)
Portobello Primary School,
Birtley, Co Durham

Harpoon

Knew you,
You warm through
The snow soft against
The memory gentle
On the pain.
Darkness here once
More and again
Hard are the walls
Around my
Head.

Rhiannon A. E.
Wakeman (15)
Norwich, Norfolk

Trust

Trust is balancing
On a rocky precipice
Undecided –
With a gently blowing breeze,
Which suggests betrayal.

Joanna Clay (13)
Windlesham School,
Pulborough, Sussex

Greed

Greed is a hungry animal,
Hunger ruling out all reason;
The more he gets
The more he wants.
Insatiable.

Heskel B. Isaac (10)
North Bridge House School,
London

Depression

This is something hidden
  within you.
Your own thoughts,
Your own feelings,
Things you've said
Meaning different things
  to different people.
People turning against you
  for false and unknown reasons.
The looks people give you,
  meaning hatred and spite.
Being turned out of things
Doing everything wrong.
All this is depression,
Something you have to live with.

Anna Gwyn (11)
Windlesham House School,
Pulborough, Sussex

'First Day at School', Rachel Hodgkinson (9)

School Rules OK

Julie loves Peter,
Peter loves Jill.
School dinners make me ill.
I hate English,
I hate P.E.
I wish school rules were made by me!
I hate maths,
I don't get this, Miss.
John asked Ann if she would give him a kiss!
Steven smells,
Can't catch me,
Oh I wish school rules were made by me!

Donna Hill (12)
Canon Maggs C.E. Middle School
Bedworth, Warwicks

Maths is . . .

Maths is worse than scrambled egg in custard.

Maths is puzzling over a sum book when it
is sunny, you're dying to get out and play football.

Maths is not taking in a word of what the
teacher says, and then getting it all wrong.

Maths is looking at the blackboard and
thinking the list of page numbers is longer
than a giraffe's neck.

Maths is looking at the clock, dreaming of
dinner-time.

Maths is scribbling down numbers which
don't mean anything at all.

Julie L. Young (11)
Freda Gardham C.P. School,
Rye, Sussex

The Observer

Illusions

The antique brown barometer,
elegantly curved,
polished to perfection
mutely observes
the comings and goings of years,
the sunshine and storm of centuries.
Below,
The colourful cardboard calendar
Stiffly curls upward,
Seeking escape from the relentless heat
of the creaking radiator.
Twelve months, petrified into a patchwork picture.
Woven light of wickerwork lampshade
cascading down the walls,
a waterfall of brilliance,
a net of gleaming fish,
dew-hung gossamer,
delicate lace of soft-hued light
and silver shadow
Stitch together
the wallpaper's scattered sprays.

Allured by streams of golden dust
a fly is sacked
into the whirlpool at their source,
fleetingly snared in wickerwork cage.
Scorched it drops
dizzily
down
drowned in the delicious honeycomb
of white light.

Nicola J. Field (12)
Tunbridge Wells,
Kent

The Deserted Shoe

Locked in a dark closet,
A draught whistles around,
Tickling the rotted, untied laces,
But the reply is a trembling groan,
From deep inside the leather,
And even when the tongue is brushed against,
It does not whisper,
For a shoe that has been locked away,
Has forgotten how to speak.

Ian Burfield (11)
Wyburn's Primary School
Rayleigh, Essex

'The Window', Delia Cardnell (11)

The British Museum General Catalogue of Printed Books (263 volumes)

Some books you can imagine talking
On the shelves, secretly whispering
In their crisp language the fluttering of pages!
But these books do not speak.
For their leaves a heavier foliage –
Packed paper two inches thick.

Or think of a tall tree, absorbing
Water from deep wells, and filtering
Light through green forest canopies:
Likewise, rooted in these stacks
And all the while drinking in certainties,
There is no doubt in these books.

But along the rows a thin coating
Of light dust-grains is furring.
Is it the books' sheer weight
That you remember, or is it rather
The deadening, discreet
Progress of the dust as it gathers?

Arnold Hunt (16)
Hendon, London
(Highly commended)

The Toy Box

The lid is scratched and torn at the hinges:
It does not close firmly and is balanced
On a squashed teddy bear, stained in felt-tip,
Missing one ear.
The box is full: so full that I can push my arm deep
And pull out a scrap of Lego stuck to mixed plasticene.
The box smells used: of wood and paint.
The contents bring a flood of motley memories:
Torn comics, depicting Desperate Dan and Korky,
Grime-covered and read dozens of times,
Bits of jigsaw, showing Mickey Mouse's ears
And Donald Duck's Shoelace,
Puppets with torn strings and missing shoes,
The Fairy Queen covered in tin foil
For the Woodman in the Wizard of Oz
(Never performed),
A board game, the rules all gone.
I think back to the days when these things were new,
Wrapped in shiny Christmas paper,
Soon ruined by eager fingers tugging at Sellotape,
Forgetting who they were from, like animals;
And then played with for years
Until thrown into the box where nothing came
out . . .
I remember this xylophone: we used to give concerts
With a pink tambourine and a saucepan lid.
So where have our children's minds gone to!
They have vanished in the mists of oblivion
Between childhood and adulthood.

Julien Foster (14)
The King's School,
Canterbury, Kent

Anthem for Youth

Why rush through our childhood,
To become the high and mighty adults
Whose calm authority hangs over us!
For we do not perceive their expressions
Of regret, as they realize just what
They sped through, not knowing their own happiness,
As their youth slipped away.

Why are we so eager to take on harsh responsibilities,
And leave our blissful innocence?
We dismiss the fun times – thinking only
Of our work, without noticing that
In 'Adult Life' there is no pocket money
For merely washing up.

Mandy Ford (12)
Dunstable, Beds.

'Looking', Helen Hudson (11)

All in Good Time

There are:

Nails to be bitten
Clothes to be bought
Letters to be written
Trains to be caught

Hearts to be broken
Work to be done
Children to be woken
And wars to be won.

Places to be walked to
Books to be read
People to be talked to
And words to be said.

Shoes to be fitted
Clothes to be marked
Jumpers to be knitted
And cars to be parked.

Plays to be shown
And scripts to be learnt
Seeds to be sown
Stubble to be burnt.

Abigail Chisman (12)
Windlesham School
Pulborough, Sussex

Noises

Bang Bang
Clang Clang
Clink Clink
Chink Chink
Washing machine's on the blink!

Karen Parker (9)
Boulton Junior School,
Alvaston, Derbyshire

Disobedient Shopping Trolleys

Have you ever
Seriously tried a
Left hand turn with
A supermarket shopping trolley?
It's impossible,
At least I think so.
As
Soon as it's got your grasp on the handlebar
Off you go, charging into
Sugar,
Pyramids of cans,
Packets of cereals,
Towers of washing powder
And
Anything,
Just anything
That's in your way.

Slaloming through the bread,
Doing accidental
Three-point turns into the curry
Seems to be
My accidental hobby.
My brother
Often pushes me
Along,so
Off I go charging into people like
Gurgling babies,
Yelling school children,
Smoking teenagers,
Kind old ladies
And
Anybody,
Just anybody
That's in my way.
I think
They should have
A new Brands Hatch
At
The supermarket.
I'd win, well
Me and this disobedient shopping trolley
Of mine.

Mark Whittington (13)
Chantry High School,
Ipswich, Suffolk

The Steam Giant

The iron wheels reinforced with steel,
Remove the crust of rust from the worn rails.
The rotten sleepers shudder under the tremendous weight.
Sparks jump on to the lineside path, which is suffocated by charred moss,
Brittle weeds collapse as they are violently sucked in by the wheels.
Floodlit signals,
And fluorescent speed limits are all that catch the eye now.
Lumps of discarded coal lie cracked and burnt on the oily chippings,
Wagons lie dead in siding graveyards.
Smoke vanishes into the starlit sky.
Groaning sleepers are left behind, as the giant monster moves on its path of destruction,
Turning wheels come to a halt, but the train still spits sparks on to the lineside path.

Stephen Gant (12)
Sunbury on Thames, Middx

Spaghetti

The orange squiggles lie
Lifeless on your plate,
As though
A modern artist
Has tried to make a
Masterpiece of
Your lunch.

Most people say:
'It looks like worms'
But in
My opinion
That's impossible,
They're too messy, too scraggly
To be worms.

This is where the
Trouble starts,
Here comes the FORK!
The pieces of orange silky wool
Wrap themselves around the
Stainless steel trident.
The spaghetti is moving in
To strangle the helpless fork
Why can't this tangle keep still?
Just behave yourself
Like a sensible meal.

Mark Whittington (13)
Chantry High School,
Ipswich, Suffolk

Junk Food

Sprouts and cabbage, beans and mince
Are good for you, *they say !*
I must confess, I'd rather eat
Junk food, every day!

Fiona H. Struthers (11)
Uxbridge, Middx

Chipperwocky

An extract from Alice through the Cooking Gas by Lewiss Carrot.

'Twas brillig and the slimy loaves,
Did grime and ghoulash in the grave;
All flimsy were the boring groves,
And the teacher of maths did rave.

'Beware the Chipperwock, my bun!
The claws that eat, the jaws that snatch!
Beware the Tubtub teacher and shun,
The frolicous Bananacatch.'

He took his vorpal sausage in hand,
Long time the greasy foe he sought –
So rested he by the Tumtum treet,
And stood a while in thought.

And as in rubbish thought he stood,
The Chipperwock with eyes of Rudd,
Came waffling through the rotten cake,
And sizzled like a steak.

One, two! One, two! And through and through,
The vorpal pork went snicker-snack,
He left it red, and with its bread,
He went galumping back.

Andrew Stevens (15)
Pudsey Grangefield School,
Pudsey, Leeds

'Elevenses', Catherine Lennon (13)

Other People

Trader

Evening drugged with amber spice
rolls thickly out over the mosquito-drone
and lures in the bobbing junks.

Opal heat-shimmer dances
moth-light on the water.

Lap waves wash the rocking houseboats
huddling under a tangle of baby wailing
cable-creaking hulls straining their pegs.

Air curdles, a sickly breath
of opium-sweet nausea.

A slap of wet linen;
sails flap against balsa
and salt-caked sandals thump on to the quay.

The Trader pulls back a battered hood
with long bone ladle fingers,
his wind-tightened face drawn canvas thin
and knotted neck sinews twitching like foam-bitten rope
beneath a tide-splashed gleam of skin-copper;

Silent, but for a squawk of gull
in sea-glazed eyes.

Catherine Skinner (16)
Hitchin Girls School,
Hitchin, Herts
(Award Winner)

Face-worker

Morning tread of boots on concrete,
Going to work like moths to a light-bulb.
Dropping below the surface
To corridors of black ice.
The noose tightens . . .

Yes, sir!
No, sir!
Three bags of top-quality coal, sir!
Cheese and pickle sandwiches,
Again;
Up and down the shaft,
Again;
Monkeys in laboratories,
Mice to feed the cats;
Give us this day our weekly wage-packet.
The noose tightens . . .

'Hangman's Rope' home first at five-to-one:
Good money on a well-placed bet,
Extra chips tonight.

Slumped in front of the telly
And the newsreaders' gloating.
Grimace as the kids start their row again.
Living for the 'Ploughman's Horse',
Mates and beer and darts –
Loser buys the next round . . .

Noose tightens,
Neck breaks.

Helen Wightman (15)
Convent of Our Lady of Providence,
Alton, Hants

'The Black Hole', Steven Pearce (7)

Street Artist

A fourth King bearing his box of rainbow,
Has settled like the sun's touch on the street,
Produced a cloth in magicinal show
And chalks flooding colours about our feet.

The woven patterns that give concrete depth,
Take shape and breath through the artist's own loom;
An innate gift, that with natural stealth
He merges the strands into shape and form.

Affinities are found with his chalkings,
Our desires. He creates a wonderland,
An equilibrium of our longings,
A harmony from deft and patient hands.

Although we stood there, wished we could do that,
Admired the pictures as we coined his hat,

His living pavements were not beyond theft,
As feet smudged out the riches he had left.

Christopher Jones (16)
Quorn, Leicestershire
(Highly commended)

The Wedding

She was embarrassed at the church,
She went all red,
And said,
I don't!
WHAT?! came the call from the crowd.
They glared from under their big fancy hats.
Feathers, veils, fruit and all
Shook with shock . . .

Judith Freeth (12)
Priestley Smith School,
Erdington, Brimingham

The Homecoming

She waited in fear,
For his homecoming.
While he drank his beer
He thought nothing of her.
The doorbell rang with impatience.
Startled, she jumped up in terror,
Slowly the chain was unlatched
And there he stood, anger in his eyes.
Walking backwards into the kitchen,
Tears flowing from her eyes,
He followed removing his
Thick, black, leather belt.

He lashed out at her, with joy;
She dared not scream;
The children were upstairs;
Too late feet pattered along the floor.
She had seen their lonely far away look,
The terror in their eyes.
Slowly they left.
Knowing what was happening.

Rachel Nixon (14)
Marist Convent Senior School,
Fulham, London

'Helena', Sarah Choonara (16)

The Liberated Woman

I'm a liberated woman,
I've even burnt my bra,
I've started eating brown rice,
And I drive a Citroën car.

I've become a vegetarian,
I've given up meat and cigs.
The only bacon I eat now
Is male chauvinist pigs.

I go on protest marches.
I'll travel anywhere
To join a really worthy cause
(If the media is there).

In the pub I drink real ale,
By the pint of course.
Then I go out with the girls
And knock a policeman off his horse.

And when I'm locked up in the nick
With a bunch of lags,
I'll spend all my working day
Sewing 'fe-mail' bags.

Jill M. Batterley (12)
Wirksworth, Derbyshire

Us Versus Them

The bells ring loud; the doors swing wide,
And out storm pupils; the raging tide
Of pigtails, freckles, old school ties,
Crisp blue shirts and new black eyes,
Pendants, rings, and snapped shoe laces,
Grubby knees and impish faces,
Streaming down the long dark halls,
Clutching bags and soccer balls.

The teachers follow, tired and weary,
In wrinkled shirts and suits of dreary
Greys and browns and pin-striped blues,
Loosened ties and polished shoes,
Exhausted from another day
Of horror pupils with tricky ways,
Who prank and jest and chance their arm,
To annoy the 'Teach', then dance from harm.

They struggle past the staff-room door,
A forbidden pass of ancient lore,
And grab a cup of sacred drink
And down it straight then start to think
Of how to gain a sweet revenge
Upon the kids and start to mend
Their evil ways of tricks and jokes,
Who delight in having fun to poke

And then they turn unto the dread
Of marking homework in pain unsaid,
Punctuation, spelling errors,
The bungling of the tiny terrors,
Little swines who've done it wrong,
Wrong page, wrong number, wrong ALL DAY LONG!
Whose repeated blunders make them groan,
Oh, they dread to take the homework home!

And while all this is going on
The pupils make a beeline home,
And laugh and smirk and scream with joy
(The girls as well, not just the boys).
This war, it shall go on and on
Unceasing, it lasts for all time long
Us versus Them, the simple way
To summarize each new school day.

Scott R. Paterson (14)
Banchory, Scotland

His Own Little World

Mr Brown,
The gentleman,
Wouldn't so much as tread on an ant,
The meek, little businessman,
Whom everybody likes.

But things are different at a quarter to nine;
It's time to go to work.
He walks out of the front gate,
Gets out his keys,
Unlocks the door and steps into a whole new world.

He puts the key in the ignition, turns it, and the . . .
His eyes turn red,
His teeth sprout fangs,
His body grows, ripping his suit to shreds.
Claws shoot out of his hands.
His cloven feet hit the accelerator.

He is the King Kong of strength,
The Ben Hur of driving,
He is ruthless.
Pedestrians beware!

The traffic lights mean nothing to him,
It's just green, green, green.
Pelican crossings, zebra crossings,
The flashing Belisha beacons,
Don't register in his mind as warnings, but as prey.

The speedometer doesn't stand for speed,
but for the number of victims.

Nothing can, or will, stop him.

And so it is.
He plays with his secret thoughts, in his own
Little world.

Ted George (13)
The King's School,
Canterbury, Kent

A Different Description

This person is a wolf in a lamb's disguise.
He's black.
If placed in the enemy's hands he would escape.
He's the stiffness of Russia
and the arrogance of Britain.
He's a restless bee always buzzing about.
He's a misty Autumn.
He's a cloudy sky with the sun peeping through.

Martyn Wollett (10)
Freda Gardham C.P. School,
Rye, Sussex

Life and Death

Consequences

Prologue
It harrows me with fear and wonder
(Shakespeare: ***Hamlet*** Act 1 Scene 3)

Unborn babies hold the world
in their unborn hands.

They grip humankind
in a stranglehold of wonder
and unborn thoughts take time
to become commands –
and unborn error only needs the future.

Fergus Martin Burdon (17)
Lincoln

Life Sentences

The days of disillusionment
Come sometime after first consent,
Before the doors of parenthood
Lock you within – for good,
for better?
or for worse?

The bitter age of misconception,
Nine long months in one direction,
Suspended sentence deep inside,
Regrets with no room left to hide.
Was this a blessing?
or a curse?
for better?
or for worse?

The final pill, the hardest yet,
A mother-child cannot forget,
Her living burden, always there
Maternal love becomes despair.
The course is set,
Was this a blessing?
or a curse?
for better?
or for worse?

Simon G. Corby (17)
Hull,
Humberside

Birth

Strange;
That something so heavenly, miraculous, ethereal,
Should involve so much sweat and tears, toil and
trouble, blood and guts.

Strange;
That a form so perfect, fresh, unique,
Should make such a raucous, obnoxious, repellent
noise.

Strange;
That a bond so unifying, life-giving, tight, as the
umbilical cord.
Should be severed, broken, divorced, in such a
final manner.

Strange;
That with every breath, twitch, movement,
The child becomes estranged, independent,
detached from the mother.

Strange; life.

Katherine Atkinson (14)
Lady Eleanor Holles School,
Hampton, Middx

Not To Get Involved

Trained, we were,
to clean and smile and take temperatures,
to prop wheezing hulks up with pillows,
to tell them (it's a nice day, Mrs Jones) useless things,
But never to get involved.

Then, one day,
A man was sitting in the waiting room.
His wife was giving birth I understood.
I knew the woman, heard her moans.
The birth was difficult,
But I told him she was all right.
Tried not to get involved.

Died, she did.
And his face crumpled in misery.
I placed the killer in his arms.
And he shuddered; silent wracking sobs.
He gave the baby back to me.
And walked out.
He never looked back.
I wiped my eyes, put on a smile,
Was once more a nurse
And didn't get involved . . .

Marina Kiely (14)
St Gregory's, Bath, Avon

Window-gazing

She watched my finger
Pointing at the window.
'Look,
There's your face,' I said.
She gurgled
And pushed her nose against the glass,
And grinned at her reflection.
Her little brown eyes shone out
From a pale face
Mirrored in the sunlight.
Clutched in her little hands
Was a forgotten felt kitten,
Damp and warm,
Misshapen from constant handling.
She smiled at me,
'Let's go home now.'
And gently pulled her hand.
She looked back at the window and grinned.

Charlotte R. Davies (14)
Convent of Our Lady of Providence,
Alton, Hants.

'Crossing the Road', Simon Holly (6)

William

One and a half
Fat cheeks
Podgy all over
Eyes brown and twinkly
Nose, red like a cherry
Bottom like a peach

William.

Hapinder Nahar (11)
Woodville Middle School,
Leatherhead, Surrey

An Adult's View of a Child

They are saplings in the wind,
And we are the oaks.
Where they see black and white,
We only find grey.
A child's page is clean,
The adult's is ink-stained.
Their swords are whetted for the world,
While ours are worn.
To them, the glass is still half-full,
To us it is already half-empty.
They are the laughing flames,
And we are the dull, grey ash.
They are the clouds that weep in the evening.
And we are the soil that drowns in the rain.

They are the crispness of morning,
And we are the peace of the night.
They are the sand washed by change,
And we hope we are the rock.
They are confused but pretend to be calm.
They ask questions that we can't answer,
And we send them to bed.

Helen Wightman (15)
Convent of Our Lady of Providence,
Alton, Hants

Margaret

Today, she sits by the cupboard door
For a change.
They've taken all she owns
And she's left with only memories;
Counterfeit people,
Counterfeit things.
She squints at the sun through the window,
Through glassy eyes
And drops of glassy rain,
For she thinks she hears the sound of a friend.
But it's not,
It's just the wind,
And the wind is lonely too;
But the wind doesn't change and people do.
She'd made it through life, stage by stage
To find her only prize
Was age . . .

Andrew Lawson Campbell (14)
Glasgow, Scotland

The Neighbour

Wizened and widowed
He lives next door.
Old yet compact
Wrinkled but still
Transparent.

Mouse-like he nibbles
Through the garden.
Ears veined
As a bat's wing
He turns sharply
At the tread
Of a stranger
Someone to talk.
Someone he captures.

Leading them in
To his yellow-papered house
His voice rises high
Excited and shrill.
Fingers fumble
With the foil of a bottle,
Spilling milk,
His eyes shine
And purple lips quiver.

Through a vapour screen
Over china cups
Eyes meet but
The mouth revolves.
So eager for news,
He never stops to ask
Of the world outside.
His empty house is
Merely shadows and
Silence.

Adam Stanley (15)
Minehead, Somerset
(Award winner)

The Aged Child

I only saw her three times
Before they took her away to be
Imprisoned and forgotten with other old people:
The price some have to pay for old age,

I remember her cottage in Norway
Beside a dark stream
Which wound freely down from the mountains.
Her life, too, was calm and gentle,
Shaded from the twentieth century.

Large telegraph poles unfurl the advancement of time
And tiny shoots have grown to magnificent forest trees,
Now bent and wrinkled.

Over the years she grew smaller –
Diminutive, but not extinguished.
She would peer at me through faded eyes and
I felt her bony, tentacle-like fingers feeling my face.
I could almost hear her arthritic joints creaking
With every move.

Once I gave her a box of chocolates.
Underneath her silver whiskers
A playful girlish smile appeared.
Her shrivelled face looked happy as she
Hid them beneath her cardigan,
With a giggle like a naughty child's.

She never knew she was old.
'How is little Else?' she asked me in Norwegian,
But Else is my Grandmother,
And it is sixty years since she was a little girl.

Fru Beckeli was one hundred and one years old when she died.
She had seen the first bicycle in the town,
The first car and the first train.
She had survived both wars.
Her children had grown old:
Now she could lie in peace.

Myles D. W. Bowker (13)
The King's School,
Canterbury, Kent

'Sikh', David Barlow (16)

When No Life is Given

Death's almost human;
  It eats, it sleeps.
Death feeds on lives
  But it has to sleep
If only for a few moments.
  For life to carry on
One has to be born
  For everyone that dies.
It sleeps and takes no lives
  When no life is given.

If death did not sleep
  Then all life would die.
There would be no one left
  To carry on life,
To carry on death.
  If death did not sleep
Then all life would die;
  But death would die;
When all life was dead
  It could not feed.

Melanie Farmer (14)
Buckhaven High School
Leven, Fife

Forty Per Cent Self

A grey-brown hand, wrapped, withered around mine,
Guided vivid wax crayons over rough-grained scrap
paper.
Two generations apart, the hands contrasted
As the colours and patterns on the surface differed.

Old as she was, she was at the top of the graph;
Time had run out.
She was to step down from her throne,
To slide inconspicuously to the grave
As a leaf falls from a tree to tan brown.
Yet she limps along
From home to the main street,
Tends a cat – her son –
And complains about the weather.
Her roses are in full bloom and so is her mind,
. . . when she remembers she has one.

Times have changed.
I guide her wrinkled hand over the fruit bowl:
Dull dead colours, just visible in sunlight.

Benjamin Eaton (14)
The King's School,
Canterbury, Kent

He Didn't Mean It, Officer

When he jumped
he didn't mean
to splatter his remains
on the ground.

I knew him, officer,
He was my friend.
He didn't mean to
actually
kill himself.

It was just that he
read somewhere
that not deciding not to live
was in effect saying
'I want to stay alive.'

But he felt he'd never
actually decided,
only drifted into
being
still here.

He didn't mean it, officer,
when he jumped.
But when he realized
he had the power
to take the decision
to end his life,
he wanted to know
how it felt
to feel the power
to take the decision.

So, he took the decision
and jumped.
and realized,
too late,
he couldn't decide
not to . . .
after all!

So,
having decided
to decide,

He died.

Helen King (15)
Chantry High School,
Ipswich, Suffolk

Not Hero: Hell's Angel

The tranquillity and peace is torn asunder
With a resounding battle-cry of throbbing thunder;
An exulting fanfare challenging all and none,
Metal charger gleaming in the sun.
Hard boots, hard drugs, hard life and harder eyes,
Hell's Angel – discarded dregs, despaired of and
  despised.
Leather jacket taut across his back,
Like hair and coat and bike his character is black.
Demon rider, he crouches on his monstrous steed,
Ripping down the road at careless speed.
Hell's Angel – a fiend in human form,
Hell's Angel – a devil lacking horns.
He sees her twisted marble, frightened face
Frozen by fear in endless time and space.
The bike sloughs round, its fabric ripped apart with
  tortured squeal,
Hard tree, hard ground, hard life, hard death, hard
  deal.
He died that she might live yet who would name
Nick Riley hero – who'd press his claim?
He was a Hell's Angel, thus sealed his fate –
Not Nick Riley, hero: but Hell's Angle, late.

Jannine Jobling (14)
Barton-upon-Humber,
South Humberside

Love and Friendship

Your Life and Mine

My love for you will break
This rock,
Send memories crashing through
The ocean's sky.
You'll walk on alone and I will
Find you screaming
In the wind.
Seagulls will swoop
Around our fiery head, calling
For our souls
And I will touch you warm and silently
At dawn and cry
For what has gone before.

It's been so long since I've seen you.

Rhiannon A.E. Wakeman (15)
Norwich, Norfolk

'My Friend', *Lee Webb (11)*

Aeroplane

I will be your aeroplane,
twisting, turning, swooping, gliding,
you can pull my controls,

and I will do tricks for you,
I will dive, dip and rise high to the clouds

and turn upside down,
I will be your
aeroplane.

Claire Bayntun (9)
Freda Gardham C.P. School,
Rye, Sussex

Space

When I am a man
I will go to Mars
With Robert
In a spaceship.
We will have robots aboard
And computers.
A shuttle will take us.
Robert will drive.

Edward Simpson (6)
St Christopher's School,
Farnham, Surrey

A Visit

I looked up from the table
And saw that spring
Had brought a stranger
To dine with us
An older sister's friend
Whose bright face
Became one with our family
Frequent visits
Lengthened and matured
Until she was living
In our attic
Permanently painting
And smiling

She was a warm mother, sister
Reassuring and confident
At night
Her voice like musk
Drowsed my senses
As she read from books
Whose titles remain unknown
Her words drifted
Peaceful as dust
Falling
In a sun-splintered room

Tempted and cajoled
By the ooze
Of atmosphere
Haze of smoke
Warmth of flesh
I ascended spiralling

To a higher room
Leaving my bed
For a vibrant grotto
Pleasing to the senses
Enlivened and enriched

Without words I was accepted
Scooped from a sea
Of turpentine jars
And oil-encrusted palates
I was cocooned in a blanket
Then tenderly daubed
On to a canvas of experience
I was honoured
A god
Immortalized

But eddies of maturity
Seriousness
And pressing homework
Stole her from me
One morning she was gone
Swept among the death-umbered leaves
She moved from our house
My sister followed soon
And I was left alone
To my books and papers
And my canvas image
Found blurred and dusted
On our deserted attic floor

Adam Stanley (15)
Minehead, Somerset
(Award winner)

Thaw

I died that time,
That time she said no,
I'd watched her from afar,
Admiring her, every curve, every movement,
The flesh soft and delicate to my imaginary touch
Her friends laughed, 'ignore' me, they said
I looked at her, she glared, her eyes, jewels of opulent
  hatred.
Her, me, never, she sneered.

Days passed,
The memories faded,
But she remembered,
We'd pass, I'd sense her shield, separating
Her from me in the corridors of the school.
The cold serenity of hatred gone from her eyes,
Replaced by a deep confusion,
She wanted me, I needed her,
But appearance had to be kept up,
Her kind, my kind, separate units,
Never to be connected, never to be seen together.
So I watched her, she watched me,
Alone yet joined,
Mingling in each other's dreams and prayers.
But never talking.

Grant Hobson (15)
Argoed High School,
Mold, Clwyd

Shy Love

I remember that disco one Saturday night.
Suddenly seeing the girl for me.
There she sat in the corner like a radial piece of light.
Her eyes blue, her hair fair.

She turned around and stared at me.
Her eyes were dazzling and lips were flushed.
My heart beat faster
My legs were frozen like a block of ice.

She broke loose from the corner,
And came out fighting on the bell,
And pounded me with her words,
She so forward,
And I so shy.

Then I stunned her.
She fell for the fatal blow,
How she wobbled to and fro.
There she stood, gloves down.
The question came out again,
'Do you want to dance?' I said.

Paul Nice (14)
Billericay School,
Billericay, Essex

Without You

Without you the house is a grey
Gloomy, blank place.
Without you that corner in that
Room is solemn and mourning.
Quietly screaming for the warm
Comfort of your body that sits
Patiently in that chair.
Without you the house is a
Soundless cave.
But most of all I miss you.
Without you your bed lies
Cold and neatly wrapped up in
Sheets and blankets.
Without you your smile, your
Laugh, your tears are shut away
In a tiny box waiting for you
To come home and open that box.
Most of all I miss your comfort.
Without you your place at
The table seems so empty, so
Clean, so missing you.

Linda Perry (14)
Billericay School,
Billericay, Essex

Combing Your Hair

My gaze rests on your chair,
Where you used to sit,
Combing your hair.

And as I look,
I see your face
White as the lily.

For your face was pale,
And your eyes,
Green as the ferns by the wayside.

I was the envy of the spirits,
And they took you for their own.

Julian Fowler (13)
Windlesham School,
Pulborough, Sussex

Even

Hot coffee steams in long
wisps toward the musty ceiling
Three minute old cigarette ash litters
the tables and floor.

To the customers
the day is the same as yesterday's
and tomorrow's
outside the sky is a vacant blue
numerous unknown figures pass
the window their faces contorted
into today's troubles
and numerous unknown dogs
scamper along the pavement
following the first face that lifts
an
eye to them.

To the customers today's coffee
will be the same as tomorrow's
and
to me today will be the same as
tomorrow, and the next day
even so I cannot forget you
that easily and your face will
haunt me
like yesterday's sorrow.

Fergus Martin Burdon (17)
Lincoln

Family and Home

If You Don't

Mum says things like
If you don't turn out your light . . .
If you don't eat your tea . . .
If you don't turn off TV . . .
If you don't dust for me . . .
If you don't drink your coffee . . .
Everyone says if you don't
I say I won't!

Dad says things like
If you don't stay in tonight . . .
If you don't stop arguing . . .
If you don't stop bickering . . .
If you don't go to bed . . .
If you don't do as I said . . .
Everyone says if you don't
I say I won't.

Brother says things like
If you don't play a game of tye . .
If you don't play computer . .
If you don't play snooker . .
If you don't give me your sweets . .
If you don't give me your seat . . .
Everyone says if you don't
I say I won't.

I say things like
If you don't lend me your bike . . .
If you don't teach me to knit . . .
If you don't stop being a twit . .
If you don't let me get on . . .
If you don't stop singing songs . . .
I say if you don't
They say we won't.

Karen Parker (9)
Boulton Junior School,
Alvaston, Derbyshire

Secret

This was my world,
And no one knew it except me.
But then Mum found out.

She followed me.
She wanted to know where I went.
She was just being nosey.
Then she told everyone.

From being the place only I knew,
It now became everyone's,
And I never went there again
Because it no longer had its magic.

The next day when she was busy,
I went out, saying I was going to play;
Really I was going to find another world,
One where I was King,
And everyone did what I said.
But no matter where I went,
And no matter where I decided to play,
Nowhere was quite the same
As my original world –
The one defiled by her.

Bruce Ashcroft (13)
The King's School,
Canterbury, Kent

The Cardboard Desk of Drawers

It stood lonely in the faded sunlight
Of the Autumn afternoon,
The silver grains of dust
Glinting momentarily in the beams.

The browned paper flaked
To reveal more aged layers
Of toy pot paint, matt and crude,
And off-cuts from papered rooms.

Each drawer revealed a tin;
Each tin revealed some stamps,
Singed by age and sunlight,
Their transparent sticky backings clouded by time.

Each tin was carefully ordered,
Containing its own little world
Of stony-faced monarchs
And things of 'national interest'.

They remain of little worth,
Like the day when they were put there
By my father in his youth,
Waiting to grow old and be antiques.

My father is older
And so are they,
But not in quite the same sense,
For no longer will he admire them,

No longer will he take them out,
Replace, position and add to them,
For they are what he was then
And he is what he is now.

They can only represent an image of him,
Fleeting but intense,
The passing fancy of a precise and sober man,
Ever-changing in his tastes.

But now the last drawer is closed
A part of time is dead.
The rusty tins stay hidden,
Awaiting rediscovery.

My father goes on living
And changing in his ways,
But a part of him remains captured
Ever in the drawers to stay.

Jonathan F. Ibbott (14)
The King's School,
Canterbury, Kent
(Highly commended)

Dad, the Cat and the Tree

This morning a cat
Got stuck in our tree.
Dad said,
'Right, just leave it to me.'

The tree was wobbly,
The tree was tall.
Mum said, 'For goodness sake,
Don't fall.'

'Fall!' scoffed Dad.
'A climber like me.
Child's play this is,
You wait and see.'

He got out the ladder
From the garden shed.
It slipped and landed
In the flower bed.

'Never mind,' said Dad,
Brushing the dirt
From the garden
Off his trousers and shirt.

'We'll try plan B, stand
Out of the way.'
Mum said,
'Don't fall again – okay.'

'Fall again,' said Dad,
'Funny joke.'
Then he swung himself up on a branch.
But it broke.

Dad landed, wallop,
On the deck,
Mum said, 'Stop it,
You'll break your neck.'

'Rubbish,' said Dad,
'Now we'll try plan C.
Easy as winking
To a climber like me.'

Then he climbed high up
Above the garden wall.
Guess what happened?
No, he didn't fall.

He gave a great leap
And he landed flat
In the crook of the tree
Right on the cat.

The cat gave a yell
And sprang to ground.
Pleased as punch
To be safe and sound.

So it's smiling and smirking
Smug as can be.
But poor old Dad's
Still stuck
Up . . . the . . . tree!

Matthew Makinson (10)
St Paul's C.E. Primary School,
Chorley, Lancs

'The Market', Amanda Thomas (13)

My Mum and I

My mum and I are different,
Because we don't like meat.
The blood we hate and lumps of fat,
So peas and beans we eat.

Lentil cakes are better
Than chunks of cow's behind.
Mushroom flan is nicer than
Some bits of bacon rind.

When we think of liver,
Kidneys, tongues and hearts,
We say we are relieved
To have french onion tarts.

Kidney bean curry with pepper,
Is extremely nice,
But we need to have some water,
With lots of ice.

My mum and I are different,
Because we don't like meat.
The blood we hate and lumps of fat.
So peas and beans we eat.

Karen Stallard (11)
Davrick Wood Secondary School,
Orpington, Kent

Nan

Nan sits quietly,
Looking.
Her most valuable possession,
A crossword book.
The pages, black ink,
Like a flicked fountain pen.
She picks it up,
And a pencil
Steadily lifts off the table.
The noise of a rubber
Like someone scratching their back.
So involved with the crossword
That everything else has gone
From her mind
A satisfied snort
And a cry of victory.
The book crashes down,
The crossword,
A mass of black, white and grey,
A complete page,
A complete life.

Helen George (11)
Halesworth Middle School,
Halesworth, Suffolk

My Grandad Working

Pulling pumps, serving,
that's my grandad.
Shouting, serving.
A maths genius
is my grandad,
totting up all the prices.
Speaking serving speaking serving.
In the mornings
getting all the barrels of beer.
I help on a Saturday
and Sunday usually.
In comes the lager, Harp,
it is here.
Here comes the bitter,
Norwich mild.
Here comes the customers,
12 o'clock, better open up.
'I'll have a bitter,'
says Jock.
'I'll have a dry wine,'
says Olly.
Loads of customers now.
Soon be closing though.

We shut the shutters
at 2 o'clock
on Saturday and Sunday.
Home we ride
after collecting
all the glasses
and putting them
in the glass washer.

Ricky Ling (11)
Downing Primary School,
Ipswich, Suffolk

The Incredible Bouncing Man

Bouncing in and out of
Death's reach, as if he were on elastic:

My Grandad.

'Stand by your beds! Here comes Grandad!'
A permanent smile engraved on his face,
Walking stick in one hand, pint glass in the other.

But annually, at Christmas time, he goes that little bit
Too far, enjoys himself just too much,
Drains his seemingly eternal energy source,
And always ends in hospital.
The family sit round his bed.

Drips sustain his energy and blood level.
His eyes are closed.
The nurses have given up.
Tears form.
Grandad is a deathly white, mouth open, just breathing.
But by the end of that week he is always better.
Four heart attacks, three years of nearly dying at Christmas,
Two weeks to live in 1960, and twenty years of chain smoking:
He would never give in to septicaemia.

He's always back, drinking, eating and most of all talking,
With eighty-two years behind him and countless years in front,
Causing scandals in his old people's home,
Asking if widows can come and stay with him.

My Grandad is unique.
And wonderful.

Andrew M. Holgate Darley (13)
The King's School,
Canterbury, Kent
(Highly commended)

'A Cobbled Street With Two Gas Lamps',
Mark Naylor (5)
(Highly commended)

Bedroom for Rent

Bedroom for rent.
Windows big . . . includes spider's web.
Handmarks on walls with mixed felt tip colours.
Wool dangling from light bulb
makes very good ActionMan swing.
Bed makes good car, ship, moon buggy, trampoline
and a warm, snug place for the night.
Natives are friendly. Includes 2 gerbils
3 fish
1 dog
plus 1 free gift (Mum).
Accommodation is compact.
Bedroom for rent.
No reasonable offer refused.

Nick Ashby (9)
Cloudside Junior School,
Nottingham

Places

The Tower Block

The tower rises to the sky.
And points down to hell.
Boarded up windows
And sprayed-upon walls
Blend silently into the cliff of grey.
A dazzling sea of glass and technology –
Pride of the council –
Is now a concrete tombstone
Shadowing those who live within.
Damp peeling walls cannot smother
The shouts of anguish and frustration.
There is no peace or privacy
In the concrete monster,
Speared through the heart
Of a town called
Malice.

Edward Beaugie (14)
The King's School,
Canterbury, Kent

The Dump

An autumn wind waved the horsetails, and a sodden
Track led to the island. In tall, lush grass, broken
Branches lay hidden. Down by the fir trees, a bird
Winged its way over the Dump.

A pile of ashes indicated last night's fire;
A hole in the rush-covered entrance revealed the camp,
Dug out of a little hillock, enlarged by
Many years of use.

Inside were buried memories: a Swiss army penknife, a
Chipped and marred frying-pan, some broken pieces
  off a
Wooden partition, old war magazines and comics –
A treasury of old essentials.

Well-worn earthen paths criss-crossed our territory,
Summer evenings spent hiding behind nettles or
  climbing ridges,
Running after the enemy, building outposts
Of imagined reality.

And then they built the housing estate.

Sholto T. S. Byrnes (14)
The King's School,
Canterbury, Kent

The Car Factory

Noisy, boring, regular as clockwork.
Lifting, bending, break your back work.
Dirty, tiring, no time for shirking,
Boss man says, keep on working.
Time clock, stopwatch, every minute measured.
Lunch time, tea break, time to be treasured.
Machinery comes to a sudden halt
Having developed a major fault.
The conveyor belt begins to slow
The assembly line breaks its flow.
The factory calms to a still,
The car output is now at nil.

Josephine E. Cox (11)
Swanage, Dorset

Air: London Underground

Every connection has its function
In this equation, an entangled junction
Of flashing lights, lines that spark electric,
That meet and part perfectly symmetric!
They gather at intervals to a focus:
Piccadilly is truly Piccadilly Circus
When through the long rush hour, and later,
Commuters turn acrobats on the escalator!

Join, then, these slow city-dwellers
Who for a moment become travellers
And watch the lines merging and emerging;
They meet and part, converging, diverging,
Converging, diverging, converging, diverging.

Arnold Hunt (16)
Hendon, London
(Highly commended)

An Election

An empty room.
A blank graph in the office.
People coming in.
Around the town are posters.
Leaflets going through the doors.
There is going to be an election.
Figures and results coming in from all over the country.
A telex machine chatters like a train.
Columns grow.
Hot bodies rush through corridors.
The room is stuffy.
Telephones ring like unstoppable door bells.
Last minute speeches.
Newspaper reporters.
We're just in the lead.
The candidate is sweating.
The graph is still growing.
Slowly but surely everything slows down.
It is the announcement.
We've won.
Celebration, noise.
An empty room.
A full graph.

Christopher Cox (10)
St Ippolyt's C. E. Primary School,
Hitchin, Herts

Playground

The misty haze
Of the morning glaze
Shimmers over the school.

The curtains are drawn,
The windows are open,
The breeze is soothing cool.

I look around,
There is no sound
Apart from the rustling leaves.

Misty black shadows
Cast down on the dell
From the towering green pine trees.

The cooling breeze,
The sunlit trees,
Gently the branches sway.

The snails move
In the murky ground,
Munching the leaves like hay.

It's time to go
From this place I know,
Feeling the damp'dew grass.

I walk away
On this shimmering day,
The trees, the leaves, I pass.

David Goodall (11)
Northmead County Middle School,
Guildford, Surrey

'School Interior', Rhian Wyn Hughes (13)

L'Herault

The reeds were tangled, cracked and brown,
Rustling and shimmering in the warm breeze
That felt like eternity.
Mating dragonflies skimmed the water
As leaves parachuted from weeping willows
And floated to oblivion.
In the glistening reflections like a poorly-exposed photograph
Weeds waved as I gazed.
I tossed a stone into the deep;
It glinted in the sun's rays
Then fell with relief, spreading ripples
Which were soon no more.
A flock of birds, their wings silhouettes,
Sped across the sky
And, as I moved away,
I thought how I was like those birds,
Moving from green England
To sultry climes.

Julien Foster (14)
The King's School,
Canterbury, Kent

Ceannloch Biorbhaidh
(Kinlochbervie)

The land here is dying,
diseased with rust and rubble.
Down in the bay,
the heather is uprooted,
the peatgrass starved out,
the stubble tilled
and the waste sown with earthmovers.
The harvest is already one
of white patios,
of hulking trawlers leering in the harbour;
stretched planks of red-grey iron.
Crofts with corrugated roofs
skulk in the shadow
of marble and classic arches.
Crofters now commute across
the wild red bogs
to Inverness,
have blinded themselves
to the blue hills –
and blind, by Gaelic law, are ineligible
to rule land:
this is proved, here,
but money is law now in Ceannlochbiorbhaidh.

Alexander Hodson (17)
Sheffield
Yorks

Kimmeridge Bay

Mist-shrouded hills covered in gloomy haze,
Distant guns boom like thunder.
A bleak, gloomy mist fills the grey sky,
A cool fresh breeze blows through my hair.
Suddenly, wings beat rapidly, as scared birds fly off.
The sea climbs softly up the beach
Making a shuffling noise.
Shale hills being eaten away by the sea,
Like a lion gnawing at a bone.
Huge chunks of limestone coated with seaweed
Cover the beach, making them dangerous for human
feet.
A cold, evil sky glares down upon me,
Making me shiver violently.

Graham Shred (11)
Northmead County Middle School,
Guildford, Surrey

Where the River Runs

Where the river meanders
Old men told stories,
And men drove chariots
Around the hill fort.
Today,
The fort is in ruins,
But we can still see
The river,
Winding its way,
Through the fields.

Richard Underwood (5)
Caerleon, Gwent

'Trawler in Newlyn Harbour',
Timothy Varlow (16)

Passing Time

Soldiers guarding,
Throwing spears,
Chariots drilling,
Wheels running,
Shooting arrows,
Children swimming,
Men training,
Sharpening spears on stones.
The alarm goes!
Arrows flying!
Chariots clashing!
Bleeding people,
Flashing swords!
Blood spurting,
Attack!

Grassy mounds,
Cold and peaceful,
Legends floating all round,
Lonely sounds
Flowing all round,
Silent hills,
Deep ditches,
River flowing sadly
Over ground
Heavy with ghosts,
And time, passing.

Christian Powell (6)
Caerleon, Gwent

R.I.P.

I fear graveyards.
All those dead people
In their wooden boxes,
Old and young
In a state of eternal sleep.
Shadows
From gravestones fall
Across the short cut grass.
'Died at 14 years old'
What a thought
To leave this world
For some other, so young.
The flowers seem so bright
For such a morbid place.
I would rather be dead
– Than in a place like this.

Sylvia Allen (15)
Buckhaven High School,
Buckhaven, Fife

Beyond Strange Walls

Beyond the wall of captivity,
A black spider crawls round a glass prison.

Beyond the wall of strange weather,
A spurt of green water.

Beyond the wall of peculiar places,
A red city of blood and sorrow.

Beyond the wall of puzzles,
Sherlock Holmes studies the black bitterness of war.

Beyond the wall of sweet honey,
Winnie the Pooh sits dreaming of songs.

Beyond the wall of the past,
William the Conqueror fights for his life.

Beyond the crumbling wall of death.
A graveyard of still bodies.

Anna J. Budd (9)
Lynsted & Norton C.P. School,
Sittingborne, Kent

Art and Music

The Rehearsal

The swelling sound of music
Came slowly into being,
Growing to the baton
The conductor held.

The power of the orchestra,
The choir's united singing,
They drew me into ecstasy
Of musical delight.

Some day I may sing in such a choir
With my voice strongly blending,
The bonded voices rising,
Snaring all who hear.

But that is in the future –
For now I'll only listen,
Captured by the music
I do not fully understand.

Harriet J. Bazley (11)
London

Mrs Power played the Tambourine

Twisting, diving,
Then a swoop.
Banging, clanging,
Loop the loop.
Ribbons tossing,
Clash and smash.

Swirl or twirl,
Dart or curl.
A flick of the wrist.
A sharp little kick.
Sometimes slow
And sometimes quick.

Robin L. Gillyon (8)
Bedgrove County
First School,
Aylesbury, Bucks.

'String Players', Miranda Zitman (15)
(Special mention)

A Musical Storm

The piano is whipped up,
Wavelets of viola
Harass the 'cello,
The kettle drums boom and vibrate,
A flash of first violin
Tears through the melody;
The storm rises,
The timpani growl menacingly,
Another roll of drum;
The crack of D sharp.
Its energy goes,
And snarling,
He diminishes to *pianissimo adagio*.

Mandy Grant (13)
Bedworth, Warwicks.

Mona Lisa

He was my father and mother,
Good side and bad side,
God and Devil.

Good old Leo.

For the penalty of eternal paralysis,
There must be, and are, compensations.
I live in a nice, big room.
In a nice, big house.
The neighbours are nice
And beautiful. The mundane and ugly
Can be only transient here.
At night, the bright lights are turned
Off, and for a pitifully few, short hours,
We sleep, without ever closing our eyes.

I am a kind of God, amongst gods,
In the presence of God (or a close facsimile thereof).
In fact,
The house is a temple. Muttering prayers,
The worshippers come. They offer gifts
On entry, and, in return, each one receives
A prayer card. However, despite the pleas
Of my priests, the assassins come;
Their sudden, bright lights work
Slowly,
And I, and all my silent fellow prisoners,
We cannot blink
Or wince.

They talk of my eyes, all of them do,
And I watch theirs.

The young men come, and, in a meditative
Trance, try to clone me,
As I sit, and watch.
And, by the million, my admirers come
To pay me homage.

Andrew J. Cowper (14)
Walton-on-Thames, Surrey

Graffiti Man

Hello,
Little man,
Scrawled up on the wall.
With your sarcastic nose,
And bold eyes,
Hello.

Wayne J. Greenough (11)
Stevenage, Herts

Postcard Poem

(From the painting 'The Window' by Pierre Bonnard)

The clustered houses form a village,
The golden coloured villas, the pink roofs of the white bungalows
The brown wooden frames hold the panes of glass in place,
The blue and purple sky swirls,
The chestnut brown photo album waits patiently to be opened,
The pale rose book waiting to be read,
The checked cloth sits upon the table,
The green wrought iron balcony bulges out from the corner of the house.
The woman pauses, motionless, staring at the peaceful scenery,
The ink pot stands to attention,
The white blank paper remains still and white,
The tissue box tucked neatly into a corner,
The sandy-handled ink pen lies quietly about to be dipped into ink.
The woman's peach face,
Her nose long and bent,
The arm long and thin.
The tall buildings glance, upright, gazing ahead of them,
The violet mountain slopes down from the skies above,
The blue hilly mountain peeps out from behind his friends.

Lynn Eldered (10)
Tunbury C.P. School,
Chatham, Kent

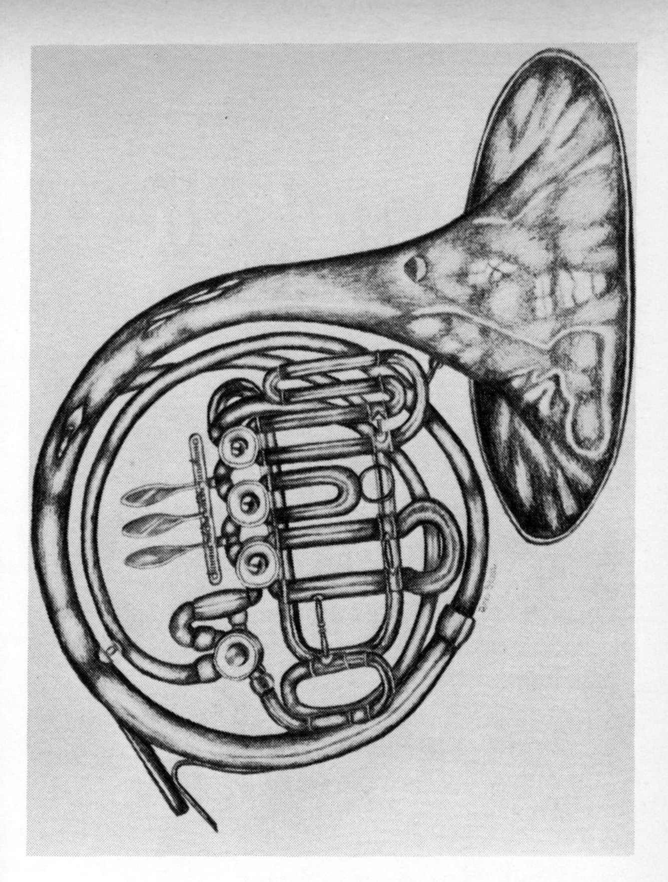

'French Horn', Ben Skea (14)

Animal Life

The Lambing

Rain tightens the fen margin
To a tremble of high-wire;
Lambs straddle the clover.

Spindly legs splayed,
Struggling on a needle-fine edge
Of earth and sky.

Caul-streaked wool glistens
As warm nostrils heave the air
And damp breath dissolves in the mist.

New-borns flounder in
A comedy of jerk-steps:
A flailing surprise of catfish grins.

And round clown-eyes;
Knees buckle, and elastic turf
Bounces up beneath them.

A fisherman stiffens in mackintosh
To clatter his rods, numb fingers fumbling
The barbed hooks and radish-fat floats.

A switchblade flick, and he casts
A flint arc scattering bite-sparks
On the swollen stream.

Farm ducks abusive,
Petticoat-swaddled washerwomen,
Waddle past the bean rows,

Wade mud-splashed into the pond
And huddle in the weed,
Moaning from the mottled sedge.

Wooden cows dot the neutral flats,
Eyes rolling placidly, tail-switching flies,
Chewing the freshly mown swathes.

Dun lowlands fuse the weather-line
And watersweet meadows spread a yawn
Into the flush of horizon.

Catherine Skinner (16)
Hitchin Girls School,
Hitchin, Herts
(Award winner)

The Countryside

One day in England's green and pleasant land,
There was a rabbit, a fox and a mouse.
The rabbit and the mouse lived in harmony together
But the fox had a liking for rabbit stew
Which was quite unfortunate for the rabbit.

However, one Sunday a pack of hounds,
A few horses and a few human beings
Who had been drinking champagne,
Came to chase the fox.
The rabbit and mouse watched as the fox
Was torn to shreds by the hounds.
They were glad the fox was gone,
Now they could live in peace together.

However, the next day in England's green and pleasant
  land,
The rabbit lay awake in its burrow,
When there was a loud rumbling
Sound; it shook the earth.
The rabbit knew its time had come
And the earth above fell upon him,
As a man in a big yellow machine drove on.

Only the mouse was left
And he chewed the farmer's corn,
Enjoying the sweet sauce that the farmer sprayed
On so liberally for him.

Gordon Dwyer (16)
Billericay School,
Billericay, Essex

The Sixth Commandment

'Thou shalt not kill,'
Mocks the horn's call.
The hunt begins.
'Thou shalt not kill,'
Pound horses' feet.
'Thou shalt not kill,'
Pumps the blood of
The fleeing fox.
'Thou shalt not kill,'
The judge intones.
'Most heinous crime!'
But is he less
A killer than
He who slaughters
Fellow men, yet
Never would cry
With our judge and
Friends, 'Tally-ho!
A fox!'? No more
'Thou shalt not kill.'
Commandment six,
Rewritten, is:
'Thou shalt not kill'
Thy fellow men,
But foxes, wild
Are game for all.'
The dying fox
Now breathes his last.
'Thou shalt not kill,'
He whispers still.

Clare Connors (14)
Debenham High School,
Stowmarket, Suffolk

Blood Sport

I chased the red confusion with my eye,
It scuttled fast, hungry eyed, across maps
Of snow. Birds rose like arrows in the sky
As it ran into thick, wet woods. Perhaps

They caught it, I don't know, I didn't stay
To watch the waves of galloping horses,
Their riders, lean and elegant, on their way
To find their fun. I only heard voices,

And they were not the shouts of red faced men.
That fortuitous sight smeared me like blood,
I kept thinking of the flexing fox, then
The chase, the bloody kill. I wished I could

Make sense of it all, feeling like I was
The hounded one, running wildly in snow;

It's 'sport', a 'show', no necessary cause –
They lost the true scent a long time ago.

Christopher Jones (16)
Quorn, Leicestershire
(Highly commended)

The Deer

Wandering endless never parting
Through the heart of highland grey,
Dancing with the purple heather,
Leave the grasses to the fray.

Running wild exhalted freedom
Bouncing sunny steps regain,
Darting as if quivering arrow,
Following in alarming game.

Poised retreat it strikes the target,
Antlers shatter tensioned peace,
Fear enlightening, eyes of terror,
Movement slows, the spirits cease.

Louise Candey (14)
The Ridgeway School,
Plymouth, Devon

'Alligator', Mark Staples (17)

Death's Doorstep

Silent,
Not a whisper of life,
Black cloudy puffs of midnight.
The mouse, sniffing,
Peering into the vast atmosphere,
Beady eyes, blinking slowly, wisely,
Up in the scaly tree top,
Spying,
Dart. Mouse leaves his hole,
Shy, creeps into the black nowhere,
Seeping down,
A gush of golden blur,
Supple feathers, clear but musty somehow,
Long black fingers clawing the air,
Chase,
Running,
The mouse scampers furiously back,
Pounding,
Back to somewhere he may never reach,
The mouse lies still.
He has rung death's doorbell,
And death answered his ring.

Emma Carey (11)
Guiseley, Yorks

Mouse

Grey shadow of nervousness
A web of twitching whiskers
Eyes like beads of ebony
Dropped in a face of innocence.
Sudden death always round the corner,
Blown like a flake of wood ash
On the brink of life.
Fate decides which way it will fall.

Gemma Woolrych (12)
Hillcross Middle School,
Morden, Surrey

A Cat

I saw a cat,
It moved slowly,
It moved quietly like a ghost.
It moved silently up by a bird,
It stopped to watch,
Its ears pricked suddenly,
Claws long and sharp.

Neil Allen (7)
Barton Hill Primary School,
Bristol, Avon

Tom Cat

Stalking the alleyways,
Hunting for food.
Rummaging through bins,
For bones and scraps.
No one notices him, he hunts at night,
Yes, he's a wise old tom cat.

Benjamin Mack (10)
Oyne Primary School,
Aberdeen, Scotland

My Cat

My cat walks carefully,
It stretches each leg,
Not a sound
No claws
Just soft paws.
It creeps to a bird
And waits.
It jumps
Fast
Like a spring.

Kelly Griffin (8)
Barton Hill
Primary School,
Bristol

'Pouncer The Cat', Daniel Cresswell (6)

A Lament for a Baby Bird

The bird is dead.
Finished.
The bird's mother
and I shed a tear.
The mother curls her long neck
in sorrow for her lost baby one.
I do not wear clothes for a funeral.
I take the bird and bury her
in a watery grave,
at rest amongst the fishes
she lived her life to catch.

Vanessa Stopford (9)
Didsbury C. E. Primary School,
Didsbury, Manchester

Garden Acrobat

Aquamarine, modest, snow-capped head,
Dusky orbs contemplate the doorstep.
Buttercup yellow laced with leaf green,
A melange of green and yellow plumage.
Agile, petite acrobat manoeuvres between the nuts.
Early morning thief spies the glistening jewel
Protecting its creamy treasure.
Pecking and tearing the shining safeguard
Until he reaches the milky goal.
Alert at all times for the enemy,
The sparrowhawk!

Angela Linford (10)
Wickford City Junior School,
Wickford, Essex

The Owl

There was an owl
Who lived in a shed.
He laid some straw
For his bed.
He played all day
And slept all night.
And flew through the air
Like gliding kite.

Jonathan Stark (6)
Moorland Infant School,
Lincoln

An Ostrich

An ostrich towering above
Reaching the sky like an aeroplane does
Pecking away at the zoo bars
Popping children's balloons
And bending spoons
You'd probably think he was a lunatic.
He parades up and down
Showing off his terrific frown
And then he flies up
And falls down like a cup
And when it's time for a bath
He squeaks and squawks
And fights and talks
And sorts his feathers one by one.
And did you know
He fought with a bungalow
And he thought he was a snail
With no tail
And gave the children a little wail
And then he went quite frail
And then he pretended he was a sail
The silly old fellow
And he said hello
To his shadow
And his favourite
Is to sit on a polo!

Jacqueline E. Hughes (7)
Northbourne School,
Didcot, Oxon

When I see a Bird

I wonder, when I see a bird,
What it's like to fly,
To glide in the limitless sky.
I'd soar above the trees and lanes
Away from this world's pains.
  I see two doves,
Nuzzling softly on a perch,
Talking and whispering,
Like two lovers on a bench,
But more polite and graceful.

Marcus Diggle (12)
St Andrew's School,
Rochester, Kent

The Bat

Take your mother's black velvet evening dress from the
  closet
And screw it into a ball,
Tie a piece of string near the top and pull it tight,
You have the head and body – all ready for the wings.
For wings you use a small pair of brother's rubber
  flippers
To hold it steady in flight.
For its brain you need a handful of darkness,
Feed it with sleep and hunting for that's all it needs and
Remember to place the brain upside down
It's more use that way!
For the voice take it to the nearest radar station
And leave it in the dish for twenty-four hours.

Take it out in the daytime because it has no eyes
So use little sister's marbles
To stare into the darkness
And into the soul of things.
Turn it upside down and shake it to bring it alive,
Then put it in the palm of your hand and watch it take
flight.

Emily Ravai (12)
St Mary's Gate School,
Bournemouth, Dorset

The Spider's House

The spider
Builds her house
Not with bricks,
Or with straw,
But with her inside.

It glitters,
It shimmers,
It looks beautiful,
But she catches flies.
In silence she eats them,
With happiness and pride,
In a house of her inside.

Danielle Sears (7)
Fern Hill Manor Junior
School,
New Milton, Hants

Dewy Cobwebs

Thin delicate web threads make a suspension bridge
in the dew.
They are fairy lights.
They are the window of a jeweller's shop,
Or a diamond necklace.
The dew makes all things beautiful
Except the bloated spider.

Jonathan Hutchings (11)
Wickford City Junior School,
Wickford, Essex

The Spider

First he's in the bathroom,
Then he's in the hall,
Then he's in the kitchen –
I can't stand it at all.
Then he's in my bedroom,
I nearly had a fright.
And then he crawled all over me
In the middle of the night!

Penny Armstrong (7)
London

Cinquain: Snails

The snails
Slowly sliding
Along the garden path
Leaving a silver trail of cold
Dampness.

Karen Sage (13)
St Mary's Gate School,
Bournemouth, Dorset

The Frog

There lives a frog
I've hardly seen,
Who lives in the rushes
Tall and green.

I heard him croak,
I saw him creep,
Then he was off
In one big leap.

Nicola Bailey (6)
Thatto Heath Infant
School,
St Helens, Merseyside

Frogs in Water

There was a splash when the frogs
Jumped in the water.
  A ripple,
  A wobble,
  A stir.
They are deaf to the songbirds
  but
When the rain comes down
And pats the water as if it were a dog,
The frogs gently listen.

Andrew Abbott (10)
Beaudesert Park School,
Stroud, Glos

The Walrus

Majestically yawns,
Protruding sharp ivory,
Gliding through water.

David Jay (10)
High School of Glasgow,
Glasgow, Scotland

Seal

Vast barrel body,
Beery face pointing skywards,
Haloed in a fine tracery of sugar-strand whiskers,
Flesh cascading in folds,
Neck scarred with tight lipped wounds.

His sinuous wives twist and turn,
Churning the icy sea
In an ecstasy of high spirits.
Gleaming black with water,
Each wearing a ruff of foam,
Spaniel eyes pleading,
Lithe ribbons round a maypole,
Their harsh barks drown the roar of the ocean
And the screaming of the gulls.

The beachmaster sits
At the edge of the creaming sea,
Wreathed in foam,
Lord of all he surveys.

Gemma Woolrych (12)
Hillcross Middle School,
Morden, Surrey

The Temperamental Tortoise

A motionless, yet delicately sculptured,
Mound of apparent solidity,
Lies triumphant, but vulnerable,
Its porcelain textured, curved dorsal surface,
Sectioned into beautifully tesselated hexagonal plates,
Each linking to form a marbled brown coat of armour,
Each bearing a faultless record of
Years gone by,
Exhibited in contrast to its mount
Of crude green vegetation.

A gentle tap,
And a tiny, scaled head,
With protruding jet-black eyes,
And skin wizened since birth,
Cranes outwards from within the case
That so many, so oddly think can be naturally disconnected,
Cranes outward in eager anticipation of a leaf,
Of fresh, succulent, nutritious LETTUCE.

Then, suddenly –
A violent, although abrupt HISSSS
A noise unexpected from such a docile reptile,
Reminiscent of a deceitful snake, or serpent
Such as the evil species that tricked
Fair Eve.
The timid creature's anterior has disappeared once
more
Concealed within a motionless,
Yet delicately sculptured mound –
of inhabited capacity.

Jane Greatrex (14)
St Alban's Girls School,
St Albans, Herts

A Tortoise

Plod, plod, plod,
Here comes the slowest animal,
Crawling the slowest crawl,
'I'm going to do a little run,
To mystify them all.'

Zara Dobson (9)
Windlesham School,
Pulborough, Sussex

Kangaroo

As she jumps across the bush joyfully
with her tail flopping heavily behind,
her baby in the warm comfortable pouch
thinks, I'm not moving.

Kim Oeser (12)
South Bank American International School, London

'Cat's Eyes', Timothy Johnson (8)

The Greyhound

The Greyhound,
aero-dynamic.
Its body
like a weight lifter's,
tummy pulled in by a leather
belt.
Its back legs
at the top,
like a joint of ham
and at the bottom
like my tri-square
in woodwork.
Its tail,
sharp,
sharp as a knife's edge.
But its head,
the shape
of a modern car.

It sits
attached to the bed
with a vacant expression
but yearning to be free.
The chain drops
and he races.

Carl Smith (13)
Halesworth Middle School,
Halesworth, Suffolk

The Making of a Horse

Take
A cloud of silvery white,
Shape it
Into a smooth soft body,
Detach two pairs of ballerina's legs
Stitch them loosely
To the body, with strands of father's fishing string,
Shoe them
With small tortoise shells and polish them up,
Capture
The foam from a spring waterfall,
Freeze it
Into the shape of a long slender neck,
Form a snowball
From the first snows of December and
Carve
The snow with delicate lines,
Pull the threads of silk from Mother's dressing gown,
Wax them
To its neck and where the tail should be,
Capture
The wind of speed and
Force it,
With a thousand years of pain and achievement and
  strength
Put it into its head to make a brain,
Attach
Nervous twitching eyes and ears and
Let it run
Wild and free with the storm.

Nerys Lindsay (13)
St Mary's Gate School,
Bournemouth, Dorset

The Unicorn

White as moonlight,
Soft as silk,
Born before time itself.
With a single gilded horn
Set into his unrippled forehead,
The unicorn stands proud
On the dew-blurred grass,
Head turned to the East,
Shrouded by mists of unreality,
Silhouetted against forgotten dreams
To which he now belongs.

His fiery eyes shine with defiance
But there is sadness in his soul
As the first spear of light pierces the clouds
And he turns to take a last look at the mortal world,
Knowing it has no time for miracles,
Rejected by civilization,
Before galloping to the horizon on golden hooves,
Drawn by unwritten laws
To the land beyond the sunrise,
Never to return.

Gemma Woolrych (12)
Hillcross Middle School,
Morden, Surrey

Lizard

The midday sun stabs the calico-faded sky,
a thin curve of yellow dust . . .

A flicker of lizard under a flat rock,
a twitch of spring-wound tail
and a surge of tautened muscle
into the lemon haze, skidding twenty feet to a
sudden stop.

Overhead, a heat-fevered smudge
of buzzard wheels speedburnt
on a shrill screech of cauterized wings.

A film of ochre powder
settles on his glistening eyes.

In the quivering bowl of air
a heat-stupor of flies hover
over the sun-bleached skull of a rattlesnake.

Flaking olive armour trembles
towards a cluster of paper shell eggs;
a spider scuttles away over tufts of stiff grass.

A clot of thirst rises in his parched throat;
he surveys his kingdom of dust.

Catherine Skinner (16)
Hitchin Girls School,
Hitchin, Herts
(Award winner)

The Green Dragon

Very big like a house,
His eyes are flames,
He is very strong,
His legs are bent,
Elbows high above his back,
Terrible claws, long, sharp,
Pointing and bent.
Bat's wings,
Skinny,
Hard skin,
Thick and very lumpy
Like a cliff.

Phillip Bowden (7)
Barton Hill Primary School,
Bristol

The Dragon

Mouth wide open
Revealing glinting,
Pearl-white teeth.
Bloodshot eyes,
Rolling, glaring at me.
Malevolent.
A flash of green scales
As the monster moves.
He lurches away,
His tongue lolling
Out of his mouth.
And I detect
A hint of sadness
In his eyes,
Could it be –
He is lonely?

Debbie Parkin (13)
Duffield, Derbyshire

I'm a Dragon

I'm a dragon but I have no puff,
I'm meant to eat people but I'm a vegetarian.
Smoke rings aren't much good when you have to do battle,
And my horn got concertinaed when I tried to spear a grape.
I missed,
My roar's more of a wheeze and I cough half way through,
And my so-called poisoned breath seeems to work like laughing gas
I wonder if you can laugh to death?
My snout is rather crumpled and
my claws are blunt as blunt,
OH! I know I'm meant to roar and rant and ravage all the land!
But I can't.

Timothy Philips (11)
Boxted C. E. Primary School,
Colchester, Essex

Eggs

Inside the angry dragon's egg,
a spurt of fiery fury.

Inside the sorrowful dragon's egg,
a drop of glistening water.

Inside the cheerful dragon's egg,
a hornful of happiness.

Inside the truthful dragon's egg,
a just speech.

Inside the thieving dragon's egg,
a mean cell of ugliness.

Inside the smart dragon's egg,
a beautiful black bow-tie.

Inside the magical dragon's egg,
a box of delights.

Anna J. Budd (9)
Lynsted & Norton C. P. School,
Sittingbourne, Kent

The Zoo

What would you do
If you went to the zoo
And found all the animals had gone?
I was truly amazed
And the keepers were crazed
Not a bear, or a lion, just none.
Not a sign of mouse,
Empty elephant house,
Whatever had happened, d'you think?
No foxes or tigers,
No zebras or chimps
No hippos there, having a drink.
Then, to my surprise,
I saw with wide eyes,
On a horse-drawn carriage outside,
All the animals dressed,
In their Sunday best –
Off for their animal ride.

Marian Lucas (11)
Blessed George Napier School,
Banbury, Oxon

The Natural World

The Day of the Daffodils

In some quiet corner of some quiet garden,
The first one appears
A drop of colour in a drab world.

Soon there comes another, and another,
A blaze of colour
Bursting and growing unstoppable yellow.

This is only the start of the attack
The advance forces
Struggling to survive in a cruel world.

It is a highly organized advance,
Like a military campaign,
A war against colourlessness.

Nicholas Perks (11)
Dalkeith, Scotland
(Highly commended)

'Flower Preparation', Allison Wells (13)

Old Flowers

Like clothes at the end of the week
Dirty, torn, discoloured.
The poppies flake their coats,
Drops of ruby red tears.
Along the dusty roadside.

Like a runner at the end of the race –
Tired. Bent almost double.
Roses –
Pink, yellow, red, stand in tatters
Looking like tramps in their rotten rags,
Bend their heads in embarrassment.

Children squeeze the petals to pulp,
Staining their fingers with colour and smell.
Grass, tangled, yellow, is dry
and harsh,
Not soft to sit on any more.
All is ready for the covering of leaves, then snow.

Caroline Hall (13)
Halesworth Middle School,
Halesworth, Suffolk

A Pepper

Dark red
Like an awkward jumbled apple.
Plump and lumpy,
Shiny hard but smooth:
A small pumpkin
With a green coat-hanger hook.

Inside
A laughing mouth
With a horrible spicy smell;
A nest of seeds like milk teeth
Hanging from orange, spongy gums.
A closed-in cave
Deep in the heart of the fruit,
Where chains of blood vessels
Are as delicate as a dragonfly's wing.

Group poem by children from
Barton Hill J. M. I. School, Bristol

Cabbage

A golf ball on a tee;
A rubbery globe
With overlapping coats of leathery leaves:
Patterns of white roads on a green hill.

Sliced in half:
A monstrous spider weaving a crinkly web;
Scrolls of paper
Or a Christmas angel.

Group poem by children from
Barton Hill J. M. I. School, Bristol

Pomegranate

The pomegranate is round like an apple
The smooth skin is golden
Tinted with rich ruby red
The sepals are hard and sharp, forming a circle on top
of the fruit like a crown
Stamens are inside brittle, crumpled
We cut it open and rich red juice like blood flows out
There are many vermillion red squashy seeds
Very sticky, embedded in a bright yellow spongey flesh
They tasted sweet   I liked them

Mohammed Morsy (8)
Lincewood Junior School,
Basildon, Essex

Honesty

Dry brittle stem
  Cream in colour
  Bleached in the sun

Sandy fruits
  Flattened circular discs
  Rustle in the wind like tissue paper

Seeds, brown and rounded
  Are clearly visible against the ligth
  Held between fragile covers
  Which peel off and flutter down like petals
  Setting free the seeds

  Leaving behind
  An inner layer which glistens in the sun like
  treasure.

Debi Saunders (8)
Lincewood Junior School,
Basildon, Essex

Conkers

Like lots of small
Light green hedgehogs,
With sharp spikes
On their backs,
Lying on the grass.
Inside are chocolate brown conkers,
Smooth, round and cold.

Roland Nicholls (8)
Arnett Hills J. M. I. School,
Rickmansworth, Herts

'Portrait of the Valleys', Angela Jones (14)

Tree

As a child
I looked to the sky
and saw
a riverweed frond
Silhouetted
Against the clouds

Rippling with the
Current of wind
It teased and beckoned
Climb up
On my shoulder
Called the tree

Clasped tight
To the giant's waist
I felt a rocking
Canopy above
Echo through age
Crinkled bark

Spiralling onwards
the slenderest bough
Boasted sights
and excitement
Worthy of heavy breath
and sweat

Crouched on a high
Wooden shoulder
I carved my name
Into the deep
Ochre skin
Deft and proud

I greened over
the raw wound
With a crumpled leaf
but the Tree
shivered
Blood ran sticky yellow
and I cried

Adam Stanley (15)
Minehead, Somerset
(Award winner)

Seven Old Men

There were seven old trees.
They made a feeble attempt to border
The field.
Either a farmer's afterthought,
Or the last in line of a wooded expanse.
Their skeletal fingers reached
For a non-existent sun.
Craving warmth that wasn't there.

Their multitude of capillary branches
Formed jigsaw pieces of the
Full, brooding sky.
They stood for years –
Sentinels against change.
They leaned, they gossiped.

A new field expansion engulfed all seven,
Erasing their inky etching influence,
And creating a modern arable desert.
No one mourned –
Everyone was blind.

Adam Moon (16)
Chesterfield, Derbyshire
(Highly commended)

The Field

The green sea of life.
Shining with the warmth
From the orchestra of flowers,
Delights the eyes of all who gaze
into its spell.
The multitude of bright coloured blossoms sparkle,
Each one a jewel,
In a dazzling crown of brilliance.
The silver, trickling stream,
Giving life to all around,
Loiters through the meadow,
Greeting the new day with joy.
A lonely, solitary tree sits silently
in the middle of the grassland,
Alive with wisdom.
The shadow cast from the early morning sun
is a refuge for the tiny, colourless
balls of dew,
Hiding from the penetrating beams of light.
A clump of trees, crouching at the end of the pasture,
Hums with the living cloud of insects,
Protected in the cool shadow of the branches.
The world of colour is radiant always,
Giving shelter to all forms of life,
Continuing the perpetual cycle of existence.

Matthew York (14)
Plymouth, Devon

Drops of Water

As the taps stand silently
Waiting for the next pear-shaped
Drop to appear,
It arrives at the end of the
Tap and pauses, and then stretches
Until it can't stretch anymore.
Then it falls towards and smashes
Against the hard surface
Of the
Sink and separates into a
Hundred smaller drops
Looking like transparent
Pinheads,   they slowly roll
Down the plug-hole.

Paul Stewart (14)
Ellen Wilkinson High School,
Ardwick, Manchester

Old Father Thames

I'm polluted and cleansed,
Forgotten and found.

My eyes are of liquid,
Garnished with mud.

I bubble and sing,
In my brooding brown depths.

I am none but myself,
My children are me.

I rage and torment.

The people who dare.

To unkindly blemish.

My stone still name.

My title, a king's.

Philippa Goslett (11)
Channing School, London

Bubbles

My bubble only lasted a second,
it floated in the sky.
It had an iridescent film that sparkled
and twinkled,
my fascinating bubble.
I watched it float up in the clouds,
shimmering as it danced.
It skipped and hopped and bobbed about.
It twirled its multicoloured skirt of pink,
blue and green.
That second was so beautiful until
it burst on a tree.
That second was so wonderful to see.

Susie Roylance (10)
Padgate C.E.Primary School,
Warrington, Cheshire

Upside Down

A boy peers over the river,
A wrinkled boy looks back,
The fish swim through his jumper
A duck swims through a flat.

A swan bends down to kiss herself,
The clouds swim softly by,
The fish walk down the pathway
A running girl tries to fly.

Natalie J. Spencer (11)
St Mary's Gate School,
Bournemouth, Dorset

Fire

At first the flame flickers
It lights up the room
Excited
I look through the flame and see
The whole world on fire.

Leanne Dean (10)
South Green Junior School,
Billericay, Essex

The Sun

The sun it beats down
It never hurts anybody
The haze of the morning crosses it
And makes an evil glow
The sun shines out until it almost dies.
Then somebody pulls black velvet over its eyes
It is DEAD to the night.

Selena Evans (13)
Cranford Community School,
Hounslow, Middx

Night

Night filled every corner,
Every crack, every house
In the street.
He ran along through
The fields, filling every
Place with darkness.
Sending the moon
Behind a cloud, sending
Fear to every house,
Covering us like a big
Black blanket.
People sleep while
He creeps over the land
And sea. Not a glimmer
Of light to be seen.
Night has just settled.
The moon comes out from
Behind the cloud, eerie shapes
Lurk in the dark.
The midnight hour has come
Come to pass. Suddenly
The sun comes up and
Kills the night for a while.

Catherine Burgum (7)
English Martyrs Primary School,
Worthing, Sussex

The Moon

The moon is a banana shape
That hangs
Up in the sky.
And when the sun
Has turned away.
The moon is there
To take its place.
To shine down on the earth
With a smiling face.
Its moonbeams are a slide
Where the fairies play.

Jamie Booth (6)
St John's C.E. Primary School,
Dunkinfield, Cheshire

The Moon

The moon is sometimes round.
A bright, silvery ball.
Sometimes a semi-circle.
Sometimes not there at all.
Sometimes hiding behind a cloud,
Or making shadows on the ground.
It follows you,
Peeps at you,
Protects you
In the dark.

Darren Kershaw (6)
St Johns C.E.Primary School,
Dunkinfield, Cheshire

Mercury Talks to Venus

Mercury said to Venus, 'Let's go for a walk,
We'll eclipse each other while we talk.
We might see Earth with its mass of life,
Or look a bit further and see Mars capped with ice,
Behind the Asteriod Belt Jupiter the giant lies,
Its Giant Red Spot is too much for our eyes.'
  'Don't look,' said Venus, 'think of other things.
Leave alone Jupiter, see Saturn's rings,
Saturn's chemicals are lighter than water,
Now let's see Uranus, that's Saturn's daughter,
It lies down on its axis and has odd days,
Not like old Neptune who has no special way
Except that with Pluto his orbit he shares,
That far distant planet without any cares.'
  'He's the smallest planet and too cold for me.
Nearest the Sun is me, Mercury.
At least near the Sun we have each other,
Staying together like sister and brother.
Venus, you're hot and you've got backward spin.
You are full of love but we can never win.
With no near companions, in other words moon,
We'll talk to each other on eclipse afternoons.'

Christopher M. Willey (8)
Haberdashers Askes School,
Elstree, Herts

'Twigs and Berries', Nichola George (7)
(Highly commended)

Weather and the Seasons

Kingdom of the Midnight Sun

The bluish-grey sun bubble
drifts in the sky-flux,
pale iris wanly diluting.

Spring loaded, the perfectly oiled seal-machine
contemplates a slick stream of movement
into the shifting floes.

Ripples of winter fat slide down
their sleek backs, sea-jet smooth;
whiskered disdain, and a flop
into liquid shadow.

Snowy owl tossed up in a flash of wind
wobbles in dagger air, frigid joints trembling,
drag-claws trailing useless in the maelstrom;
torn lungs strain leaden flight
breath-gasping through the rush of ice-squall.

The icebear stretches a groan
and his frost-flecked coat shudders,
sleep-stiff limbs bending slowly
in an ache of consciousness
as he lurches unsteady on to the tundra.

A bundle of lemming furtively sucks
the trapped melt water,
brush-wire fur bristling with rime
amongst the pungent herb cushions.

Little star-flowers tangle in a winking mass
across the hard ice-rind, fragrance-numbed,
stubborn roots clinging in the crawling lichen.

Wolf-howl laces the bleak plains,
and a termite-swarm of caribou
pound over the long cry of wasteland.

Catherine Skinner (16)
Hitchin Girls School,
Hitchin, Herts
(Award winner)

Jack Frost

Jack Frost
    is cool.
His breath is icy
His fingers sparkle
He draws patterns
As he goes by.
  He touches the roads
  And cars skid.
  With his spiky feet
  He touches the grass
  And tips it white.

Steven Winson (6)
St Johns C.E. Primary School,
Dunkinfield, Cheshire

Jack Frost

Jack Frost comes,
He makes thing change.
Icicles hang down.
Trees look like fairy trees.
Puddles are like skating rinks.
And on the line
Shirts are stiff – like statues.

Lara Turner (6)
St Johns C.E.Primary School,
Dunkinfield, Cheshire

A Snowy Day

Soft, white glistening snow lying
everywhere
And wherever we go
You are there
You are silver white
Touching us with frostbite
You are icy, you are cold,
You are icy, you are cold.
You are like a bed-sheet,
Crunching down at our feet
You are sparkling on the floor
Waiting at the doorstep
            at the door,
Snowflake, snowflake,
Falling down,
Wearing a white dressing gown.

Matthew Jackson (7)
St Peter's School,
Nuneaton, Warwicks

Thunderstorm

Rain is falling
down,
down,
it sparkles
flashes
pouring
splashing
diamonds on the window pane

Lightning flashing
It shines up my bedroom
And it streams through the air

Thunder crashes
Roaring
Banging
Noisy
Smashing
Thumping
Drums beating

Danielle Brown (7)
Springdale First School,
Broadstone, Dorset

The Winter's Rain

I watch the sleek rain as it taps on the window,
I wait until one drop becomes too heavy.
It tumbles down the pane and drops on the sill.

A coating of grey varnishes the road.
A car rattles by,
Its wheels slashing the street.

The sun hides modestly behind a thick black cloud,
Peering around every so often.
Then there are thin shafts of light silhouetting the trees.

Next door, the washing someone forgot to bring in
Heaves and flaps noisily in the wind.

I see the young daffodil shoots
Reaching ambitiously to the sky,
But they are being discouraged by the rain.

The house grows silent, save for the wind and rain.
I see a stray cat huddling under the fallen tree.
It sits, tucked up neatly like a warm loaf.
It looks with hopeful but pitiful eyes,
Stealing my sympathy.

Alison Everns (12)
London

Winter

Drops of forgotten snowflakes perspiring in a windowsill,
The clear, sharp smells of an icy day,
The crunch of cornflakes and eggshells underfoot,
The muffled yelps of children at play.

The dripping of a burst pipe sadly lacking attention,
The splash of the slush all over the pavement,
A lost glove imprinted into the ice,
Noses red with the overpowering cold.

A snowball, splat against the wall,
A yell of hurt pride,
Fingers blue and numb with cold,
Skeletons of trees, bare against the horizon,
More snow falling softly.

Laura Gray (11)
Allans Primary School,
Stirling, Scotland

'Milton Combe', Stephen Hyslop (17)

Winter

The snow was pelting,
                    drifting,
                    melting,
Soft and feathery,
Winter weathery,
Floating and
Flurrying and
Free.

The wind came crashing,
                      whirling,
                      dashing,
Bitter and freezing,
Icy and wheezing,
Nipping and
Whipping
Me!

Helen M. Shires (7)
Bedgrove County First School,
Aylesbury, Bucks
(Highly commended)

Winter

It was on a windy day
When the wind was blowing,
The wind was blowing the leaves from the trees,
Roaring like a wild beast
Charging through the town.

The sun was shining like a pot of yellow cream,
Spilling its light
On the frozen earth
Where the shining frost
Lay sparkling on the grass.

Kevin James Johnson (7)
Bedgrove County First School,
Aylesbury, Bucks

Haiku Summer Weather

On a warm morning
A boy's ice cream melts and drips
Down his clean blazer.

Richard Steel (11)
Beaudesert Park School,
Stroud, Glos

The Waste Ground
After T. S. Eliot

I The burnt sand

The season of August throbs, basting
Sun-bronzed bodies, laid
In rows on the baking sand, and cooled
By the shortlived morning breeze.
Summer's torrid swelter burns, causing
Plants to grow then wither, selling
Ten thousand ice cream cones.
People walk, half blinded
Dans les yeux, le soleil brille.
We stepped out, into the sunshine,
Squinting at its fervid glare; pausing in the shadow pool
Of our para soleil, we doze while our respite creeps
away.
Nous crainons ni le chaud ni le froid.
And when we leave that murky shade,
I squint down to the sea, and plunging
Into its dark depths, green, experience
The void, free of heat and cold.

Matthew C. Finlayson (13)
Macclesfield, Cheshire

Haiku

Brown, green and yellow
Leaves, fluttering on to wet
Grass to lie and die.

Julie Nicholas (8)
Manaccan J & I School,
Helston, Cornwall

The Autumn Field

Rooks and starlings smother the stubble-covered field,
Scavenging for remnants of the harvest.
Overhead a ragged V-shape of geese are bravely flying against an unyielding wind,
While swallows and swifts head south, away from a bitter Autumn day.
A tractor starts to plough the barren field.
From the cab, the driver sees a pale covering of mist
Beginning to conceal the mountainside.

Benjamin Mack (10)
Oyne Primary School,
Aberdeen, Scotland

A Violent World

Heroes

A man can only die once
But a hero can, and must, die many times.
The everyday person falls every day
Unnoticed, ignoble, but with dignity.
A hero does not die every day
But his death is repeated
To remind the minds of the nation;
They're paralyzed,
Fleetingly,
But over and over again.

Five hundred ordinary men die
Together; and the nation reels
But the next day boards a jet and forgets.
Seven heroes die
And the film reels unwind
As millions mourn for themselves;
They need to see tears to remember how to cry.
Until the memory fades in time
Like the parachute of hope they saw
Falling over and over again.

Twisted bodies hauled from mangled wreckage
The country winces – and turns away.
They weren't there at the time so it's not important.
A fireball in the sky, live on television,
The nation goes into shock.
But the press want to know
What the President said,
And can't accept silence
At a 'major malfunction',
Asking over and over again.

Sophie Kyle (17)
Slough, Bucks

Rough Justice – Fair Fight?

Red-nosed radicals bellowing in the snow,
Strike-hungry miners backing the no-go.
Cruel little wide-boys canning little kids,
Drunken, drippy students banging dustbin lids.

Cold comfort houses, decaying all the time,
Troll-like tramps treading the bread-line.
Teenage mums with moaning mouths,
Slashed wrists and blazing rows.

Paunchy politicians polishing off the port,
Imposing army generals building forts.
Posing, preening film-stars squealing for fame,
Bungling, blind scientists, life is just a game.

Over the sea, and far, far away,
Pitiful little children with no time left to play
Are counting grains, and hunting life in the dust.
This fight is fair? Carry on with your little fight
If you must.

Carys Davies (14)
Kidwelly, Dyfed

'Harmonica Player', Michael Salvage (17)

Not Any More

Before the barbed wire were beautiful and colourful
  towns and countrysides,
        Not any more,
Below the barbed wire grass grew in clumps in pastures,
  farms and gardens,
        Not any more,
Above the barbed wire was a blue, clear sky with puffy
  clouds and summer birds,
        Not any more,
In front of the barbed wire were lush forests and fresh,
  green spinneys,
        Not any more,
Beyond the barbed wire was a hilly horizon covered by
  a patchwork of fields and forests,
        Not any more,
Near the barbed wire black horses, flocks of white sheep
  and herds of dozing cattle grazed,
        Not any more,
Behind the barbed wire people laughed gaily with joy
  and happiness,
        Not any more,
Beneath the barbed wire farmers dug, ploughed and
  planted seed for many days,
        Not any more,
During the barbed wire was a bloody hell smelling of
  death,
        Not any more,
After the barbed wire was a poppy,
        Please, not any more.

Robert A. Dineen (11)
Chesham, Bucks

Belsen

The chandeliers glistened and turned to music
And while the men danced
Their cups overflowed
And amid the Golden Apple
The core rotted.

The huts, drab and grey,
Stood lifeless as the bodies
Strewn, decaying like the vanquished
In sick and pointless war.
The silence deafened.

Those that walked
Spread their skin on their bodies as best they could,
Paper people, searching mounds of dead for food.
Caged humans,
Caged animals.

The wind rattled among them,
Spitting disease.

When the animals were freed from their cages,
When the cruelty ceased,
When the huts were burned,
Hell remained.

Patrick Brothers (14)
The King's School,
Canterbury, Kent

Visual Negatives

See the man writhing at
Your feet.
See the woman screaming for
Her child.
See the soldier crack
His whip.
The blood spills; the pain kills.
The children cry; Does God know why?
Guns rat-a-tat-tat.
Truncheons crunch, thump, smack.
Bones smash, break, snap.
Do you know why?
'Ah, it is a war documentary!'
You say.
Oh no.
You are wrong
This is here
This is now
One is black
One is white
This is apartheid.
That's why.

Yen-Yen Teh (14)
London

Rhythm/Truth

Movement.
Somewhere slight,
somewhere the greedy white
male dominator
is shifted from his perch.
He feels the lurch
of discontent –
unsteady,
he's not ready
to fall from his mountain
of profit and loss.
So he strengthens
its foundations again,
not knowing not seeing
that it's when
the raw earth is built up again
from scratch
by men amd women
black and white;
in right
they'll build
then
his fear, his nightmare
of falling from his money
will be fulfilled
because toil
is on the boil
blood
is hot
among brothers
and sisters;
the ulcers and blisters

of capitalism's
last illness
won't kill us – we'll thrive
we'll survive.
people will guide their lives
themselves
there'll be no middle man:
just honest hands.

Alexander Hodson (17)
Sheffield

Battle

Two armies like two creatures
Engaged in battle,
Blood and pain,
Desperate men shouting and yelling,
Clashing and smashing,
Destruction, agony, squeals,
Blood stains,
Fear.
They yell and kill,
Sickening sounds,
Slash and cut and thrust,
Death,
Horses screaming.
The battle ends,
Destruction is left.

James Casswell (7)
Brown's School,
Sleaford, Lincs
(Highly commended)

'American Footballers', Gary Butt (14)

Violence

A violence called on me yesterday.
it stood in the grey street, where the leaves rot
– it was an impressive violence –
made of stark strips of iron, concrete and bones, sheets of flapping steel,
it bleached the land around it, blackened the faces of the people,
choked the streets, blighted harvests.
the land turned to an autumn of brick and metal.
so it stood, ankle-deep in its own burning, waiting for me,
on my doorstep.
grabbing me by the collar,
it spoke of bones and breaking, of blood and gas, of horror
and dust, of rubble and alarm-bells, of pain and blindness.
I tried to slam the door
but it waved papers – it had a warrant – it had come for the rent – it was selling something.
it clasped me by the hand,
appealed fervently to my Morality, my Sense of Humour,
it called itself Progress, Righteous Causes, Necessity, even Entertainment.
it chilled my blood, cracked my voice,
it stank of death and hate. I threw it out.
it hit the pavement with the squeal of embracing cars.
it clambered to its feet, brushing down its clothes.
I will be back, it clamoured.
it has friends in high places, so I think
I'll be seeing it back again.

Alexander Hodson (17)
Sheffield

Dooley's Sister

Inspired by 'Dooley is a Traitor', written by James Michie

Dooley's sister stood, displaying her charms,
Behind the bar of the King and Queens Arms,
A soldier came in and told her a tale,
Of a friend he knew who'd received some mail
From a brother in prison who was in for ten years,
For killing a man whilst drowning in beers.
'He was in the same cell as a man with objection
To war, though I think he was in for protection,
Because people like that are more yellow than Japs,
Right, Chaps!'
This made the soldiers give a loud cheer
And get out their wallets to order more beer.
At this Dooley's sister took offence, I fear,
For she gave the poor soldier a clip round the ear.
Said she, 'Watch it mate, my brother's in prison
'cos he wouldn't fight and charges have arisen,
He wouldn't kill a man that he didn't know,
So off to the prison that judge made him go.
I think it is he that should be locked up,
And not let out until his time's up,'
At this all the soldiers threatened to go,
Why shoudn't he fight they wanted to know,
The landlord came out to settle the row,
And said, 'Come on lads, it's closing time now.'

The row unsolved, the soldiers departed,
Why the hell had this stupid war started?
The pubs all closed early, the streets were all filled,
And down came a bomb, so the barmaid was killed.

Paul Falshaw (13)
Lady Lumley's School,
Pickering, Yorks

Flames

Some see patterns in the fire,
I see faces.
Some see the future
In crystal balls,
I say there is no future for man.
Some feel secure in the
Knowledge they're protected
I just feel scared,
Knowing that one day,
The world could go.
Just like that.
Millions of years' work,
Disappearing with the
Touch of a button.

Debbie Parkin (13)
Duffield, Derbyshire

Russian Roulette

They sat opposite;
A table in between.
Illuminated, the gun lay cold.
The lean grey Eagle raised
The weapon to its forehead.
It pulled the trigger – nothing.
It smiled.

The Bear did the same,
A click came forth,
It grinned.

But,
What neither of them realized was,
That neither of them could win

Because,
A Dove had plucked the
Bullet from the chamber.

They sat at that table for
Infinity.

Adam Moon (16)
Chesterfield, Derbyshire
(Highly commended)

'Red Indians', *Tom Lamb (7)*

Impartial Observers

Researcher: Sarled Crin Haw.
Report concerns: Species 109, 325, 478.
Home Planet: Terranius.
Species (type): Mammal, bipedular.

In their little travelling compartments, they believe that they are safe
And heroes, as they poison their atmosphere (intolerable without protection).
From A to B in nine point three.
They file into ranks on the long, thin tarmac
According to rank, speed and size.
And here, by night, the white-eyed hornets swarm under yellow-eyed dinosaurs.

They do not have to think, in general. (Perhaps it is harmful?)
Their thoughts and opinions come tailor-made to the makers'
requirements. They are sometimes given
'Truth', and there are many mediums of providing these lies.
One, common, is a magic box,
Controlled by two opposing factions.
The boxes change their face,
The time, the place.
They live and die easily, at a whim,
Many times.

For this they will live, fight and die.
This compulsive obsession, not a principle. (They are
severely
Deficient in these.)
Paper or tin. Metals are granted status and value
Not by usefulness; rarity is the yardstick.
The longest-prized is put in the mouth
Or used to cover or compose the toys of the rich.

Their democracies are, naturally, run by the
Experienced, who are, were and will be
The leaders, the respected, the consulted, the wise.
Corruption is always hidden behind a façade
Of normality.

They despise their own kind
Because they were born rich, poor
Or elsewhere.

The killing never ends. When it becomes
Too public, they award it a title: 'War'.
They hold 'war' over land, or cultural disagreements,
And the people are fed lies and enmity by the
Leaders
Of both sides. Truth is
Inapplicable, sanity elsewhere.

The competition never ceases, not at any level.

They cannot populate elsewhere in the Universe
With themselves; weapons are a different matter,
And so they choke the planet with themselves,
Localizing the infection of life. Beauty
Is given no quarter. Nature becomes
A deadly yet defenceless enemy, in war they are
winning,
Killing themselves in victory.
The concrete monoliths seethe with dead life. And the
six-armed skeletal
giants carry their burden of power,
Obliviously, perhaps, dissecting the landscape.

They drown reality in drugs.
Some choose liquid, a slow poison,
Taken alone, or in clubs.
Others inject themselves into temporary heaven,
Or smoke a smokescreen to hide behind,
Or sniff the flowers of Paradise,
To ignore the stench of decay.

They cope with mortality
By living for the present.
Species given name: Homo Sapiens.

Andrew J. Cowper (14)
Walton-on-Thames, Surrey

Dreams and Fantasy

A Television Crew in my Room

This morning I woke to find a television crew in my room.
They weren't there last night when I turned out the light.
The producer is on the bunk bed bossing the crew around.
There's a man filming up on the light.
'Action.'
'Roll.'

There's a desperate chase round the bedroom.
I decide it's best to crawl under my bed.
Oh no, there's a polar bear here, he's in the next scene.

Nadia Bagwell (9)
Freda Gardham C.P. School,
Rye, Sussex

Enchantment

It was December.
On the lawns of Cannizaro
The winter sun tinted the grass
With pale gold.

My brother and I
Climbed out of the valley
From dark and cold to warmth and light.
From turmoil to peace.

We lay on the grass
In utter content.
The warm breeze stirred our hair;
Birds voiced idyllic delight in song.

'Perhaps this place is enchanted,'
I said, and it seemed
The utter and natural course of things;
And we dozed.

I made my way
To three great trees
In a magic triangle.
'And this is the heart of it,' said I.

We sat on the brilliant grass
Beneath the trees.
And my brother said,
'We must keep some of it.'

So we took three branches,
One from each tree,
And we went.
And our hearts were full of peace.

Though we were lost
We had no fear.
I knew
Surely soon we would find our mother
Again.

Harriet J. Bazley (11)
London

'Can Can Dancers', Merrywood Boys School Group Work (12)
(Highly commended)

Dance of the Thirteen Skeletons

In a snow-enshrouded graveyard
Gripped by Winter's bitter chill
Not a single soul was stirring –
All was silent, all was still,
Till a distant bell tolls midnight
And the spirits work their will.
For emerging from their coffins,
Thirteen bony apparitions
Now commence their spectral show
Gathering in the moonlight,
Undulating to and fro.

They shake their flimsy shoulders
And flex their fleshless knees
As they nod their skulls in greeting
To the penetrating breeze.

As they form an eerie circle
Near the gnarled and twisted trees,
They link their spindly fingers
As they promenade around
Casting unworldly shadows
On the silver-mantled ground,
And their footfalls in the snowdrift
Make a soft and spooky sound
Remnants from the creaking rafter,
Sounds of disembodied laughter,
Come to haunt your soul hereafter
From the dark and distant past!

Gillian Oliver (11)
Calderchilt Primary School,
Glasgow, Scotland

Witches

Witches are mean
not to say
I hope you don't
Meet a witch today.
She flies on her broomstick
and whirls her spells
and cackles
and laughs
And magics herself away
And hides for the rest of the day.
She wears a cloak
A pointed black hat
A spider on the end
of that.
She carries a wand
And whirls it on children.
She likes children stew.
She probably would
Like you
In her stew!

Victoria Allen (7)
Springdale First School,
Broadstone, Dorset

The 13th hour

In the 13th hour,
Brick became lava,
And houses sank.

In the 13th hour,
The TV flashed with light,
And lightning forked through the sky.

In the 13th hour,
The moon darkened,
And the stars let out a howl.

In the 13th hour,
The tap dripped with blood,
And animals breathed fire.

Simon Rice (10)
Freda Gardham C.P. School,
Rye, Sussex

'A Good Goal', David Holmes (6)
(Highly commended)

Eternity

Come and watch, as the parallel lines,
So long, so teasingly always apart,
Lovingly intertwine.

Just take a free can of the perfect gas,
There isn't any charge because there isn't any mass,
And paper notes and coins would float
In a very different way. Just vote
For freedom ('cause there's no other candidate here)
At eternity.

Roll up, for the root of minus one peepshow,
You shouldn't really miss it, but you don't have to go
Just now.
Because there isn't any hurry, 'cause there isn't any
  time,
There's no standard to conform to, no routine you've
  got to mime
At eternity.

You can watch, as Universes fade and die,
Or peek at the interesting recursion of Pi,
Stroll through a Quasar, traverse a Black Hole,
But don't take it all too seriously; that isn't your role
Any more,
Not here.

You don't need to say you've lived because you're
  never going to die,
Just relax and let go, let your brain drift and fly
To the Heavens
At eternity.

There's a pair of crystal spheres, both exactly the same,
You can check them all you like, but it's totally inane
Because there is no difference, no flaw to detract
From them, as they bathe in the light they refract.
Just relax, don't lie back because your body didn't last,
Watch the beauty of the merging of the future and the
  past
At eternity.

But the Perpetual Motion Machine's out of order;
It just sits there, perpetually still in a corner,
And it never rusts.
And it never fades.

Andrew J. Cowper (14)
Walton-on-Thames, Surrey

Index of authors

Index of titles

The 1987 Cadbury's Poetry Competition

The Cadbury's Books of Children's Poetry contain about 200 selected entries from children of all ages and are illustrated with work from the national Exhibition of Children's Art.

If you would like to enter the 1987 competition whether in the Art, Craft or Poetry sections, you can write to this address for an entry form:

Cadbury's National Exhibition of Children's Art
Granby
Altrincham
Cheshire
WA14 5SZ

(Please enclose a stamped/addressd envelope)

Remember – you not only have the chance to feature in the *Cadbury's Fifth Book of Children's Poetry* but also to win a place on the Cadbury Italian Art Tour.

Also available from Beaver Books

The Cadbury's Third Book of Children's Poetry